NEVER

SAY

COMRADE

NEVER

SAY

COMRADE

by

PETER ESTERKA

VANTAGE PRESS

NEW YORK   WASHINGTON   HOLLYWOOD

SECOND PRINTING

DEDICATION

This work is dedicated to all those who gave their lives for their belief, especially to two outstanding priests who influenced my youth: the Rev. Jaromir Porizek, pastor of my home parish, who died in 1965 after serving twelve years in prison, and the Rev. Antonin Zgarbik, S. J., rector of the Bishop's School in Brno, who died in prison in 1966; both died as the victims of communist dictatorship.

The author wishes to express his thanks to Mrs. Mary Butschek, the Sisters of IWBS, the Salvatorian Sisters, the president and members of KJZT, and to all those who helped in publishing this book.

CONTENTS

1. Liberation?   11

2. Aftermath   20

3. The Sickle's Assault   28

4. Inveiglement   36

5. Futile Efforts   48

6. The Internat   56

7. Discourse   66

8. Under Surveilance   73

9. Ideology   85

10. Heroes   92

11. Trial   99

12. Workers' Paradise   109

13. Firm Resolution   124

14. Stalin Is Dead   142

15. Companionship   161

16. Interim   169

17. Foolhardiness   177

18. Betrayed   192

19. "Goodby"   200

20. Escape   205

   Epilogue   219

NEVER

SAY

COMRADE

1. LIBERATION?

Childhood is not a time for war. But still war was everywhere. It enveloped my early years in a haze of grim reality and hopeless fear. For six years the Germans occupied Czechoslovakia. Under their ruthless military domination, our efforts to free ourselves seemed futile.

Finally a wisp of hope arose on our horizon. The few who were fortunate enough to have radios kept us closely informed of the Allies' progress. It was evident that the war was coming to an end, and the Russian armies were on their way to set us free!

We could hardly wait to greet the Russians. They were of the same Slavic race as we, so we had every reason to hope that they were of the same general nature. We thought their arrival would mean the end of our subjugation. Their coming enkindled in us a new hope and a renewal of our dignity as a nation. I remember hearing the adults talking with great enthusiasm about their coming, and I, myself, wondered what I could offer them as a token of my gratitude. It was indeed a time of great anticipation.

By the early part of April, 1945, we could hear the rumble of artillery in the distance like a far away thunderstorm. Each day we could hear the sounds of battle coming closer.

The Germans were well prepared for a fierce battle. They had planned to make the Russians pay dearly for each mile of land they took. Throughout the town and in all the neighborhoods, everything—machine guns, cannons, artillery— was set up in readiness.

Compared to my childish expectation, the course of battle disappointed me. I was nine years old and, in my fantasy, I had pictured war the way I had seen it in the movies. In my imagination, I could see myself running from trench to fox hole braving the exploding shells all around me. I could hear ricocheting bullets whizzing past while I defied all danger and personally helped to rout the enemy. Instead, throughout the whole battle, I clung to my mother in a deep underground shelter.

During the occupation some people had dug shelters expressly to be used for protection during the battle of liberation that they hoped someday would come, while others utilized the existing cellars.

The shelter which we occupied was an immense cellar that had been built by my maternal ancestor many years before as a wine storage place. It was shaped like a cross with the nave perhaps 50 meters long (162 feet), 4 meters wide (13 feet), 2½ meters high (8 feet), and 5 meters underground (16 feet). My ancestor had been a connoisseur of wines, who went to great pains to store them properly near his vineyard, which accounted for the great depth of the cellar. He had also used this huge cellar as a storage place for his potatoes and other perishable crops.

At the head of the cross, a fake wall had been built as a camouflage so that the Germans could not tell there was another chamber beyond. If the Germans tried to arrest us, or put us in forced labor groups, or worst of all, annihilate us (as they did in many places in retaliation for partisan activities), we could go into the chamber through the secret opening that could be easily closed, and we would remain there indefinitely if need be.

The walls and curved ceiling of the cellar were constructed of brick; the floor was packed dirt. On the left side of the nave, potatoes were stored; on the right side were empty wine bins. Food and what medical supplies we could gather together were stored there. Great beams had been brought in to support the ceiling of the cellar in case of bombings. Even though we were very far underground, nothing was left to chance. Those who sought shelter there also brought along

12

their most prized possessions and sentimental keepsakes.

A few days before the impending battle, a parade of sixty or so relatives and close friends moved into the cellar with my own immediate family, consisting of my father, mother, my six year old sister, Anynka, and me.

Make-shift beds and tables were set up. People of all ages were gathered there, and the drone of old voices in conversation mingled with the crying of babies. Nerves and temperaments would have been strained under similar conditions, but instead, everyone was exhilarated to know that the yoke of bondage was soon to be lifted.

By the second week of April, 1945, the front lines had moved in upon us. The Russians advanced rapidly from the east and halted at the edge of the village. The main army skirted the village along the southern edge and came upon it from the west, where our shelter was located about a mile and a half west of town, deep under a low rolling hill. The hill that protected our shelter commanded a wonderful view of the village. As the main army maneuvered into the village, the forces that had stalled, waiting for the main attack, closed in from the east. The Germans' only retreat was to the north. Some of the men who had ventured to the door of the shelter could hear shrapnel hitting the brick wall which had been built as a deflection in front of the door.

It was surprising that the Germans did not make use of their carefully prepared demolitions. As it happened, a German observer had been set up in the church tower with a telephone to relay news of the approaching Russians. He kept relaying news of their progress, unaware that an assistant priest, who was hiding in the church, had clipped the telephone wires. Before the Germans could repair the wire, however, the Russians moved in swiftly, capturing the village with very little opposition. Casualties were light on either side; only two civilians were killed. One was shot by a German in a runaway attempt, and the other was hit in the head by shrapnel.

13

The first Russians entered the village around four o'clock in the afternoon. In no time, Russians could be seen everywhere.

Almost before the smoke of battle had cleared, one of the first Russian soldiers in the area cautiously entered our shelter to make sure there were no Germans there and noticed a girl (who was with my family in the bunker) was wearing a silver watch on her wrist. He asked her for the watch and she gave it to him gladly, saying, "Keep it as a remembrance of our liberation."

Then she went to her box of valuable belongings and keepsakes, that she had brought along the shelter, and took from it her cherished gold watch which she had got as a confirmation gift. She hardly had it on her wrist, when another soldier saw it and asked for it.

"O, no, I couldn't possibly bear to part with this watch. It is the dearest thing I own. My mother gave it to me for my confirmation and now she is dead. Please don't take it. Besides, I just gave another watch to a soldier," she pleaded.

But the soldier was unable, or unwilling, to understand, and he tried to grab it from her. She started to scream at his roughness. That made the soldier very mad, and he roared, *"Davaj casy lebo ja tebja strilaju* (Give me the watch or I will shoot you)."

These men were not at all what we had expected. At first we thought the war had made them as they were. Soon, we were not sure. They were a wild, heartless breed, bold to the extent of being foolhardy, ruthless, uncouth, and completely uneducated.

Indicative of their character and mentality was a young soldier of about fifteen. Before the mop-up action was completely over, some of the men could see this boy from our shelter. He was not tall enough to be a grown man and yet, there he was, far from home with a cigarette dangling from his lips and a sub-machine gun in his hand. More experienced soldiers tried to protect themselves against sniper fire by

14

staying close to the existing buildings and taking whatever cover they could. Whether it was from ignorance, arrogance, or utter defiance, I do not know, but that young boy disregarded all caution, and boldly walked in open view of his enemies. One of the men from the shelter called, "Take cover. You are an open target for the Germans. You will surely be shot if you don't."

"It doesn't make any difference. These are plenty more of us," the boy called back.

It seemed incredible to us that anyone could be so completely insane.

Late in the evening of the day of the battle, when the fighting was beyond the village, my father decided to go to our home to see what damages had been done to it.

"Wait until tomorrow, Pavel," mother pleaded.

"Nothing can happen now," he said. "Not even a stray bullet could harm me any more. They are a good distance away by now."

"Please stay here. There is nothing like being sure. You can go there tomorrow and see."

"All right!" he agreed, as he usually did when Mother asked in that particular tone of voice.

The next morning I awoke early, arose, folded my bedding, and put it into its proper place. For once I washed without being told, ate without the need of being reprimanded, and was unusually courteous even to my little sister, Anynka. I shadowed my father everywhere he went. I wanted to make sure he did not leave the shelter without me. I knew from past experience that if I behaved and looked at him with a certain wistful look, he would not refuse me. He knew from past experience, too, that my unusually good conduct was for his benefit, and he did not have the heart to leave me behind when he went to inspect our house.

The mile and a half to our home seemed like no distance at all. The village looked very much as we had always known it. Along the way we noticed a few damaged buildings and a

15

few craters in the ground made by the artillery, but overall not too much damage had been done—thanks to the priest who cut the telephone wires. The sight of our home was the best sight of all. Except for a few broken windows and a little shattered plaster, it was unharmed.

We went to the door, and just as my father reached for the knob, we heard Russian voices come from within. We listened a moment and then Father knocked a little gingerly.

The door opened, and a huge Russian soldier stood boldly in the doorway.

"What do you want?" he growled in Russian. From the expression on his face, we quickly saw that we were not welcome.

"This is my home," my father explained as he offered his hand.

The soldier ignored the friendly gesture and snarled, "Come on in, then."

My father was a little taken aback at our reception, but he took my hand and we went in.

We were shocked to see the inside of the house. It was a complete mess. The soldiers' equipment was scattered everywhere. They were cooking dinner and dirty dishes were still sitting around from breakfast. As I glanced around at the jumble, I was glad my mother had not come along with us. She would have been furious to see the home in which she took such a pride, looking as though the whole battle had been fought under its roof.

Loud talking and laughter came from the bedroom. My father didn't say anything, but started for the bedroom. The burly doorkeeper stepped in the doorway and would not let him enter. I could see the change in my father's expression as he said, "This is my home. I have a right to see what is going on in there."

The soldier pretended not to understand and stood steadfast.

An officer appeared in the doorway of the bedroom and asked crisply, "Who's there?"

Except for the Germans, I had never seen a foreigner before and I was curious about each new face I saw. To me, the officer from the bedroom looked very fierce. Like the rest of soldiers, his head was shaved; his sallow face and slanted eyes gave evidence of his Mongolian origin. He wore a crumpled light uniform and staggered around the room in his bare feet.

"What's going on here?" he asked the soldier.

The soldier answered in Russian, so we were not able to understand everything he said, but when he finished, the officer motioned us into the bedroom.

I clung closely to my father as we entered the room that had been so familiar to me all my life. Sitting at the table were three soldiers and two officers. On the table were many bottles—some empty, some toppled over with small puddles beneath them, and some still held vodka or wine. The bedroom, too, was in complete chaos. Unbelievable as it may sound, the soldiers had caught the dozen or so hens that we owned, and had cooped them up in the wardrobe in the bedroom. The floor was littered with papers; cigarette butts and empty bottles were everywhere. Sub-machine guns, rifles, shoes, boots, belts, and other equipment were strewn all around.

What would my mother have thought!

"What do you want here?" demanded the slant-eyed officer as he sat down at the table and unsteadily poured another glass of vodka.

"I am the owner of this house. I came to see if it has been damaged," Father said in an exasperated voice.

"You bourgeois! You capitalist! You are an enemy of the working class," the officer shouted.

"No, that is not so. I am a working man. I work in the factory," Father tried to convince him.

"I do not believe you. You are a capitalist, you bourgeois," he growled as he slammed the bottle on the table.

We later found this attitude to be typical among all Russian soldiers.

Like all Russian soldiers, the officer thought that anyone who owned a comfortable home must be a capitalist, an enemy of the working class.

"Bring me some vodka," the officer bellowed at my father.

"I haven't any."

"Then bring me some wine. You must have some wine. I know that you you have plenty of wine. I, myself, saw vineyards on the way to the village. Bring me some wine or I will kill you."

"I don't have any wine. I don't even have a vineyard. I am a factory worker, not a farmer."

Hearing that answer the officer's face reddened, and with a furious look, he rose and grabbed my father by the collar. Pulling him very close to his face, he threatened, "In thirty minutes you will bring me fifteen quarts of wine. If you don't, I will find you and put a bullet in your head. To make sure that you *do* return, I will keep your son here."

He motioned to one of the soldiers, and before I knew what was happening, the soldier held me securely by the arm. I tried to resist, but to no avail. Father attempted to come to my rescue, but the officer picked up his pistol and snarled, "Stand still or I will kill both of you."

My father stood motionless, deciding it was best not to resist a drunken Russian officer.

The soldier pushed me into the pantry and locked the door behind me. I could hear my father leave . . .

I sat on the floor in the dimly lit pantry. It was all such a paradox. Only moments before we were so happy to come back to our home, and now after such a short time, there I sat—a prisoner in my own home. Our liberator had made a jail of the home of my birth.

I did not know what to do. It was impossible for me to escape. There was only one small window in the pantry and that was very high for a small boy. Beyond the only door, I could hear the soldiers laughing and talking. There was no chance of escaping that way either.

I was numb with fear. My stomach was like a rock, and I could not breathe; I was not able to cry. I don't believe I even moved. At that moment I did not think of myself; all I could think of was my father finding the wine and returning.

Sure enough he did return. My father had never let me down before, nor did he this time. Somehow he found the demanded quantity of wine and was able to get back.

When the door was opened, I flew into his arms. I thought the ordeal was over, but I was mistaken. The soldier ordered us into the bedroom again.

The officer poured some of the wine into a cup and ordered, "Drink," as he gave the cup to me.

I sipped a little and handed it back to him.

"Drink all of it," he commanded.

"But I don't want anymore," I replied.

"I said 'Drink!'"

His face turned red again. He got really violent. Apparently, he was not accustomed to being opposed.

"He is afraid there is poison in the wine," father whispered to me. "Try to drink it."

I did not like wine and it took a lot of willpower to drink it all.

Apparently the officer was satisfied when it was gone.

"Here, I will give these to you now," he said as he removed two bullets from his pistol and handed them to my father. "These were intended for you and your son."

My father picked them up. I'll never forget the expression on his face!

Perhaps to this very day he still has those two bullets as souvenirs of our "liberators."

2. AFTERMATH

The initial front lines moved on and other soldiers followed. Sometimes their reinforcements spent the night or even a few days in the village, sleeping in the homes of the civilians who were still in the shelters.

We boys thought it was most exciting to mingle with the soldiers and to act grown-up, smoking the cigarettes they offered us. (Of course, our parents did not know of such escapades.)

I especially liked one young Russian soldier named Oleg, who was from a small town in the Soviet Republic of Ukraine. He let us ride his horse, kept us supplied with cigarettes, and was always joking with us. Because the Ukrainian and the Czech languages are very similar, we could understand Oleg whenever he spoke slowly. When we did not understand, he tried to pantomime. It was fun! We were very much impressed by his wild stories and his good nature.

It happened to be Oleg's birthday while he was in our neighborhood, so his comrades, the soldiers, gave a birthday party for him. It was a gay, cordial affair with accordian music, singing and dancing; vodka flowed freely. As a special surprise for Oleg, his buddies invited his old friend Vasja, a soldier from Oleg's hometown. Everything was just fine until Vasja started an argument with Oleg over some trifling matter. Both men were drunk and the argument grew violent. Vasja became enraged, drew his gun, and shot Oleg to death. The party ended abruptly and someone went to report the occurrence to an officer. The officer came to the house where the party had been held and asked, "Which one of you shot him?"

Vasja was pointed out. Without another question or a trial of any kind, the officer whipped his pistol from its holster and shot Vasja.

The next morning Oleg and Vasja, the two young friends from a faraway Ukrainian town, were buried in the city cemetery without the honor of a military burial.

Some of the other memories of those first days that are very clear to me are of a lighter nature. It was not uncommon to see a soldier with watches from his wrist half way to his elbow. It seemed that the booty which fascinated the soldiers most was timepieces and bicycles. Mr. Malik, a lawyer and family friend, told us that he had an old, wornout watch that did not keep correct time. He met a soldier who complained that the hands of one of the many watches he had stolen did not move. The lawyer looked at the watch and realized it was an expensive timepiece. He shrewdly told the soldier, "Look, see how the hands on my watch move. Here, I'll trade you this watch of mine that runs very well, as you can see, for that one of yours." Delighted, the soldier swapped watches. The lawyer took the watch from the soldier, and as he had suspected, all it needed was winding.

Instances like these were most commonplace. Soon everyone was grimly joking about the Russians' mania for watches, clocks, and bicycles.

One widely circulated story was about a Russian who stole an alarm clock and put it in his backpack. When its alarm went off, he threw the pack on the ground, yelling, "*to cort, to cort*" (That's the devil, that's the devil). He grabbed his sub-machine gun and riddled the pack until the alarm clock stopped ringing.

I suppose the funniest incident I remember of those first days was about my friend Vlada and his bicycle.

One day soon after the Russians' arrival, a group of boys was playing in the street. Vlada, who was a bit of a show-off, was trying to impress the others with his skill and daring. He rode his old bicycle in circles up and down the street, coming as close as he could to an object without touching it. To make his exhibition more impressive, he whistled a tune and kept his hands in his pockets. A Russian soldier on a much newer bicycle happened by. He noticed Vlada's antics, and slammed on his brakes and stood watching the performance. Vlada saw that he had an attentive audience so he acted even more reckless.

"Hey, come here, boy!" the soldier shouted.

Still whistling, with his hands still in his pockets, Vlada came riding up in a cloud of dust and with a terrific screeching of brakes. It was a grand finale to his performance.

"Give me your bicycle," ordered the soldier. When he saw that Vlada hesitated, he shoved the newer bicycle toward the boy saying, "Here, I'll trade you."

Vlada got on his new bike and disappeared as quickly as he could before the soldier changed his mind. The soldier got on Vlada's old bicycle and began to pedal off. He put his hands in his pockets in imitation of Vlada, and *wham-m-m-m!* Down he went. He got up, muttering to himself, and started off again. As his hands left the handle bars, he started to whistle as Vlada had done. Again he hit the ground with a thud. We folded over with laughter. He stood up, scratched his head, and looked down the street, but Vlada was gone. The last we saw of the disillusioned soldier, he was pushing the bicycle toward the market, limping and cursing as he went.

After a few days, we moved out of our shelter into our homes. Everyone's belongings in the homes had been ransacked. The soldiers took whatever booty they cared to, as soldiers have done all through history. Possessions were scattered all over the town. One would find a quilt or a chair in someone's yard all the way across town or anywhere in between. Citizens went from street to street, picking out their belongings as they found them. It was a blessing that people were honest and took only the things which belonged to them. We were all in about the same circumstances because the Nazis had already taken everything of real value. What they had not stolen, the Russians had.

The Russian general staff decided to make its headquarters in our village, and the civilians were ordered to evacuate their homes again. The wine cellar became our temporary home for the second time. After two weeks, we were allowed to return and start to clean up and rebuild whatever damage there was.

Generally, there was much happiness at that time because many of our friends and neighbors, who had been in Nazi concentration camps, began to return. But not all home-comings were joyful; not all of those who were taken away ever came back. Of the 350,000 Jews in Czechoslovakia at the beginning of the war, only 40,000 survived.

Mr. Swartz, one of our Jewish neighbors who returned, brought us the grim tale of what had happened to our friends and neighbors, the Michners, who had been taken away by the Nazis.

The Michners and my parents had been long-time friends, and my sister and I grew up with their daughter, Stelinka. Stelinka's grandmother had been like our own. Our families were very close—the only difference was that the Michners worshipped in a synagogue.

After the Nazi subjugators made all Jews wear the stigma of the Star of David on their arms, the elder Michners withdrew from public view into the privacy of their home, but Stelinka still came to see us daily.

One day Stelinka came to our home in tears. "We must move," she cried. "Tomorrow morning we must report to the Gestapo." Everyone knew that when the words "we must move" were spoken by a Jew, it meant that he was being sent to a concentration camp.

My parents immediately went to our old friends to try to comfort them. Mr. and Mrs. Michner tried to assume a veneer of optimism, but the grandmother was more prophetic. "The end is inevitable," she sobbed.

So it was.

Mr. Swartz returned and woefully related what had happened to the Michner family:

"Within a few weeks, the grandmother was dead. The

ordeal of leaving her home and the brutality of our captors were more than her old body could stand.

"Somehow the rest of the Michner family and I survived the beatings and starvation of prison life until the last days of the war.

"Then, in a frantic last minute effort to liquidate the inmates, the Nazis divided us into groups for extermination. They did not care if husband and wife or mother and child were separated—just so each group contained a certain number of people. The Michners became separated in the shuffle. Stelinka was in a different group from her parents. I was in the group with her parents. Knowing they were doomed to die, and wishing to die together, her parents begged me to trade places with Stelinka. It mattered little to me with which group I died. After all, I was alone and I found no comfort whatsoever in my companions in death. So I exchanged places with Stelinka. The Michners' group was the last to be exterminated.

"Before my group could be sent to the ovens, the Americans broke through the lines and appeared at the gates of the prison.

"Thank God, I was saved!"

A young priest of about thirty, who was from my native village, was also among those who returned home. He had been imprisoned for several years and survived the horrors of the concentration camp and tuberculosis, only to come home to die a few days later in the arms of his mother.

Many other families lived in hope that their loved ones would return. Finally, that hope faded and died. Their families never knew what happened to their own who had been dragged from their midst for crimes which they never committed.

That was the fate of Mr. Cestar, one of our school teachers. He was a member of a partisan group that was arrested only a few months before the end of the war. The night the Gestapo came to arrest him, he could have easily escaped, but he realized that his wife, who was imminently expecting their second child, and his small son would have been dealt with very harshly, so he remained and was taken away—never to be heard of again.

These are cases that I, myself, was actually aware of, but history records innumerable atrocities committed against the Czech people: 500,000 Czech patriots were sent to concentration camps and 700,000 workers deported to Germany. The Nazis obliterated the town of Lidice in June, 1942. All 200 male inhabitants were killed; the women dragged into German slavery; and the children kidnapped. The misery and unhappiness endured by the Czech people is beyond the scope of the imagination.

Finally, the war was drawing to a close.

At last V-E Day came!

Thank God the nightmare of Nazi oppression was over. It was time to forget the terror of the past and begin to build a new life.

After a year or so, the Russian army of occupation was gone. The war was history and the tremendous job of rebuilding what the Nazis and the war had destroyed was undertaken.

The people were happy! We thought we were free again!

The universities were reopened; the organizations—especially those for youth—worked excellently in the education of the youngsters.

But freedom was not complete. We Czechs were in the Russian zone, and in February, 1948, the freedom of the Czech people was taken away again, this time by the communists.

I was too young to understand the full impact of what was going on in February, 1948, but from the reaction of the adults, I knew that it was something terribly important and serious. It wasn't until I was older that I understood what really happened.

To get a true picture, one must bear in mind that Czechoslovakia had been betrayed at Munich, ravaged by war, and occupied by the tyrannical foreign Nazi army for six years. Her constitutional government was exiled in England, leaving her with only a puppet government within the country itself.

During the last days of the war, a small southwestern portion of the country near Pilsen was liberated by the American army which, for some unknown reason, withdrew to the border when the Russians advanced, leaving Czechoslovakia in the clutches of the Reds. While the aim of the Americans was to destroy Nazism and end the war, the Russians already had political designs on the future of Europe.

The sphere of Russian influence on the Czechoslovakian people at the end of the war and immediately thereafter was tremendous. Political pressure caused President Edward Benes to return home via Moscow where he was compelled to reconstruct, according to Stalin's wishes, the Program that he and his government had previously prepared in London. The revised Program (known as *Kosicky vladni program*) was favorable to the communists and was proclaimed on Slovak territory in the town of Kosice at the time when the Nazis still occupied the western part of Czechoslovakia.

The elections of 1946 resulted in a coalition government under Communist Klement Gottwald, who had spent the war years in Russia learning communist tactics and preparing the strategy for leading Czechoslovakia under Moscow's domination.

By the end of 1947 and early 1948, the Communist Party, which was the leading Party, openly flouted the *Ustava* (constitution) by flagrantly breaking its democratic spirit.

In an effort to force President Benes to extirpate the communists, the representatives of the democratic parties, the National Socialistic Party and the *Lidova strana* (People's Party), threatened to abdicate. Under the master Russian schemer, Comrade Zorin, who was sent to Prague directly from Moscow, the communists manoeuvered President Benes into a position where he was forced to accept the abdications. The communists took over the entire government by a coup on February 22-25, 1948. Those three days the communists' armed militia marched the streets of Prague, ready to fire upon unarmed citizens as they did when students demonstrated against their actions.

Czechoslovakia was again occupied by tyrants. President Benes, being only a puppet in the hands of the communists after their take-over, resigned on June 7. Gottwald succeeded him.

The communist police began to purge the parliament, the political parties, the press, radio, universities, and the schools. Many political prisoners were sentenced to twenty or thirty years, or even to life in prison. Many people escaped from the country into the West; many others were executed.

Again Czechoslovakia was under the dictatorship of a foreign power, this time getting her orders from Moscow instead of Berlin. Terror and suffering were back again after not quite three years of liberty.

3. THE SICKLE'S ASSAULT

Just when does a priestly vocation begin? What is it that actually prompts a boy to want to be a priest? Only God Himself knows for sure.

In my case, perhaps the first seed of a vocation was planted when I was very young and my father would spend hours with me at night, telling me about the universe with its moon and stars, and the glories of God who made them. Bible stories became my fairy tales and my adventure stories. He had a way of telling stories so vividly about Noah's ark, Abraham's sacrifice of Isaac, Moses, Joseph, and many other biblical personalities that they seemed to come to life. The pictures he showed me of the Christ Child in the temple, of Saint Peter, the horrible face of Judas at the last supper, the crucifixion, and others made a life-long impression on me. This was the beginning of my education.

I loved these times with my father and the wondrous doors he opened for me. Even though he did not have the opportunity to get a good formal education himself, he was very wise in many ways and wanted me to have a chance to scale the intellectual heights he could not hope to attain.

But, like most young boys everywhere, I loved the thrill of sports better than the drudgery of school. Soccer (a game as popular in Czechoslovakia as football is in the United States) especially appealed to me. Since I disliked sitting for hours to study and memorize, I often left my homework to play soccer with my friends. As a result, my grades in grammar school were not so outstanding as my soccer playing.

From the age of about eight, I particularly loved being an altar boy, and made it my responsibility to be at weekday Mass frequently and always at both Masses on Sunday. In our home, every priest was respected and I never heard one word against him. Consequently, I thought that perhaps being a priest would be a cherished vocation. Somehow, from the very beginning, I felt the priesthood was a life of sacrifice and of great responsibility. But the final decision of my vocation was far from settled.

The Bishop of our diocese realized there was an urgent demand for well-trained lay leaders, as well as priests, so after the war, he opened a Catholic high school in Brno, the capital of Moravia. Since this was the only Catholic school for boys in the diocese, it was a combination high school and minor seminary. The school was designed for accelerated students with high standards to meet the ever increasing needs of the Church. My parents and my pastor were most anxious for me to attend this school in order that I might get a higher education, and perhaps they had a secret hope of my finding my religious vocation. I, myself, was not aware of a priestly calling at that time—who can at such an age?—but I was happy to be accepted by the school. So, at the age of thirteen, I was sent to Brno to be trained by the Jesuits.

I was placed in the second class at the school, experiencing all the nostalgia of every other young boy away from home for the first time. Since I had attended a small school in a village where the standards were not particularly high, I experienced very great difficulties in my studies. I had to study very diligently to catch up with my classmates. In the beginning, my grades were quite poor, and had it not been for the patience of my teachers, I would probably have been sent home.

Another draw-back was the fact that I spoke Czech in a provincial dialect. I was mocked and laughed at by the other boys. Their ridicule made me feel very bad, but I was determined to fit into the new life. The Jesuits were very good to me, as they were to all the boys. They understood my problems and helped me as much as they possibly could.

Slowly I began to adjust to the other boys, the studies, and

29

the whole environment. Before long, I actually began to enjoy life at school.

The second year was a happier one; my studies were very much improved; I was placed in charge of the students' store. I still loved soccer and I also took a great interest in track. I played these sports every chance I had during our free time, and became rather good in both of them. I practiced hard, won several events in track, and was on the first soccer team.

By the spring of my second year, I felt that life in general was quite good. Soon school would be out for the summer vacation, and I was looking forward to my visit home with my family and all the plans I had made for the summer. I went to bed on the night of April 13, 1950, with a wonderful feeling of well-being—not knowing that night would be one of the most memorable nights in my life.

About 2 a.m. the light of our dormitory was suddenly flashed on. Imagine the reactions of twenty-five sleeping boys who were suddenly awakened by three men who wore the hated leather jackets that were the symbol of the S. T. B. (Communist Secret Police)! The three men entered the room, trying to conceal their revolvers in their pockets. We were young but still we had an idea of what was going on.

One man stationed himself near the light switch, while the other two inspected the room. When they were convinced that there was only a roomful of startled boys, they nonchalantly said they had come to check our sleeping accommodations. We were not so stupid as to believe such a story as that, and we fully realized the implication of what was meant when each of us was made to answer: "What is your name? Place and date of birth? Parents' name? Where do they live?" The replies were recorded in a notebook by one of the secret policemen.

The men left with a sardonic "Goodnight" and a warning not to enter the corridor.

Who could sleep after being awakened in such a manner?

At first the dormitory buzzed with subdued whispers. Gradually, the speculation grew louder. The most adventurous students sneaked to the door, and one even slipped out into the corridor.

"Where are you going? Get back in there immediately," came the gruff sound of a male voice.

"But I have to go to the rest room," stuttered the surprised student.

The light in the corridor was turned on and the student recognized the man as one of our recent visitors.

The rest rooms were at the opposite end of the corridor, so the boy was able to pass the room of the dean of studies.

"The dean's door is sealed with tape," was the report he brought back to us.

Naturally, the rest of us wanted to see the dean's door for ourselves, and soon other boys "had" to go to the rest room. The guard could hardly refuse us, but he stationed himself by the stairs so no one could escape. Up to that point, escape had not occurred to us.

Around 7 a.m. we were allowed to leave our dormitory. It was only then that we discovered the extent and the seriousness of what had actually happened. All the professors and superiors, all the brothers and priests in our school had been arrested during the night. (We learned later that the Church throughout the entire nation had been ravished. Only a very few religious, who worked with the sick and old, escaped the onslaught of the hammer and sickle.) The arrested were allowed to take only the bare essentials. Then they were herded into large transport trucks and taken away. Years later, I learned that the rector of our seminary died of tuberculosis in a concentration camp at the age of fifty-three. He was a very intelligent man, fluent in Russian, German, English, and other languages. He was an excellent preacher, educator, and professor, but he was in the way of the communist takeover of young minds, and he, as so many others, was expendable.

We also found that the upperclassmen had been even more rudely awakened than we had been. Their visitors made no pretense of concealing their revolvers in their pockets. They brazenly flourished them until they were sure there would be no trouble from the older boys who slept in smaller dormitories with ten boys in each. They were questioned in the same manner we had been.

On the morning of April 14, the school was without superiors. In their stead were the secret police, who wore the hated leather jackets. The two hundred students of the bishop's school waited in vain for Mass to be said. Usually classes began at eight o'clock, but that bleak morning there were no teachers, and the professors who came from town to teach were not allowed to enter. There was nothing to do. We just milled around in groups, talking about what happened the night before, and speculating about the future.

"All students will gather on the field in front of the college where an inter-class tournament of soccer will be organized," blared the loud speaker. Such an announcement, under normal circumstances, would have made the walls swell with echoes of cheer and enthusiasm. But not that morning. There was no cheer anywhere at all in the Bishop's school.

Since we were ordered to go, we went. But we went either silently or in quiet, serious talk. Nor did the game itself dispel this gloom and foreboding that had permeated the whole school. We played, because we were ordered to do so. No one was interested in the outcome of the game. At the slightest opportunity, the students would huddle together in groups to discuss the situation and the fate of the professors and ourselves.

About noon we were allowed to enter the building only long enough to eat. Then we were again sent outside for more soccer until 6 p.m. When we returned to our dormitories, everything looked as we had left it, but, upon closer scrutiny, we could see that our desks, chifforobes, and night tables had all been searched.

32

Instead of the cheer and feeling of well-being of the night before, we went to bed terribly lonesome and sorely scared. We missed our Jesuit friends, and wanted the comfort and security of our families and homes.

The second day was like the first—quiet and full of foreboding. Again we were denied the privilege of Mass because there was no priest to offer it.

During the second day, the police and militia were replaced by a group of civilians. Only the leader of the whole action, Comrade Zahradnik, stayed and became the director of the boarding school, the seminary, and the day school. Our new tutors were men we had never seen before, but the insignias on their coats denoted them as communists.

The communists adhered to their predecessors' time schedule, but everything else was changed. The cross was replaced by the communist red star with the hammer and sickle. The catechism classes were replaced with the doctrine of Marx, Engel, Lenin, and Stalin. Instead of the usual fifteen minutes of spiritual readings in the evening, we were indoctrinated in: the importance of the socialist state; the necessity of factory norms being fulfilled; the necessity of fighting against capitalistic exploitation and American imperialism; and the interest of the communists and the Soviet Union for happiness and peace for all the people; and other such unbelievable "doctrines."

Another thing that I personally could not abide was their demand that we address each communist by the title of "Comrade." Because it connoted my contempt, I could bring myself to refer impersonally to a communist as "Comrade," but I had great difficulty addressing anyone by that name.

After a few days, the usurpers agreed to allow a priest from town to celebrate Mass for us. The Blessed Sacrament was left in the chapel as before, and our prayers became more fervent.

As was the habit of many students, one of the upperclassmen stopped by the chapel for a visit during an afternoon break in classes.

He was shocked at the sacrilege being perpetrated on the altar before his eyes. Standing at the altar with a set of scales were a member of the S. T. B. and Comrade Zahradnik, the new director of the school. The locked tabernacle had been broken open, and the consecrated hosts were spilled out onto the altar cloth. The chalice, monstrance, and ciborium were conspicuously sitting on the altar. Since these vessels are rich in gold or silver plating and often have jewels or semi-precious stones set in them, the communists were evidently interested in their monetary value.

"Don't you dare touch those things. In God's name, get away from the altar immediately," the boy shouted as he rushed toward the men at the altar. He was shaking with holy indignation and rage.

"Who do you think you are talking to?" haughtily inquired Comrade Zahradnik. Trying to regain his composure, the student stammered, "What do you think you are doing here? That's no way to treat the consecrated hosts and vessels."

"We are your superiors now. We will give the orders. As for you, you had better get out of here before I arrest you," the secret policeman in the leather jacket warned.

The student saw it was useless to argue, so he left and ran to the school.

"The new superiors have broken into the tabernacle," he called to his fellow students. Before he could finish his incredible story, the whole group swarmed toward the chapel. The news of the desecration spread through the school like wildfire.

The intruders were just weighing the ciborium when the doors flew open and the first group of boys streamed into the chapel.

The students were horrified at the spectacle of the hosts scattered all over the altar. As if by command, they all knelt on both knees and bowed profoundly. They wanted to amend, at least in this humble way, the sacrilege committed against God in their chapel.

The two intruders looked up in amazement to see the adoration of the students. Before they could finish weighing the ciborium, the most daring of the students charged at them and pushed them from the altar.

By that time, the entire student body was in the chapel. In imitation of the upperclassmen, we all knelt down in solemn adoration.

Seeing the temper and resolve of the students, the two men slunk out of the chapel.

After their retreat, two students slipped into town to summon the priest, who was allowed to celebrate Mass for us, to gather up the consecrated hosts that still lay scattered on the altar.

In reprisal for their action, not one of the first arrivals in the chapel was allowed to finish his studies for a degree. The student who discovered the desecration and informed the others was treated the worst of all. As a punishment, he was expelled from school, was refused admission to every other school, and was denied the completion of his studies.

When my parents heard what had happened at the school, they came and took me home. I had not gone there to be a communist or be re-educated in their ways. I left two months before the school year was over.

At the close of the school year, all remaining students were notified not to return after the holidays. The Bishop's school, along with his hopes for dynamic new priests and laymen, was suppressed.

It is rather ironic that in less than a year after that communistic sacrilegious action, Comrade Zahradnik committed suicide in one of the buildings of the seminary he had tried to "re-educate."

35

4. INVEIGLEMENT

"I'm looking for the principal," I said to the man in dirty pants and faded shirt whom I found in the physics and chemistry lab. "The teacher told me I could find him here."

"You must be the black sheep, the one for whom our school was not good enough," the man commented sarcastically.

I ignored the man's sarcasm; I asked again if he could tell me where I could find the principal, Comrade Stika.

"I am the principal," declared the man.

I was surprised because I did not expect to find the principal dressed so shabbily. Trying to hide my surprise, I introduced myself and asked if I could continue my studies there.

"What can I do? It's the law that you finish the necessary education. Since this is your home town, I suppose you have to go to this school," he retorted coldly. "I understand you are in the eighth grade."

"Yes, sir, I am."

"Comrade Pavlik is your home-room teacher. Go to see him."

That was my introduction to the new principal of the school I had previously attended. Since there were still two months before the summer vacation would begin at the end of June, I had no choice other than to finish the semester in my home town school.

It was in the afternoon that I tried to re-enter the school because my parents had just brought me home from the Bishop's school in Brno, I went directly from the railroad station to the school. Needless to say, I was a bit apprehensive as to how I would be accepted by the school authorities and even

36

by my fellow students. The coldness of Comrade Stika's reception gave me a definite feeling that I was not welcome there. But I obeyed his command to go to Mr. Pavlik.

As I entered the classroom, my old school friends greeted me with a big "Hurrah." The warmth of their greeting reassured me. As I looked at their faces, I noted that only a few new students were among my old classmates. It did not take long at all before I felt accepted and completely at ease with them.

During the next few days, however, I noticed many changes in the school. Not only had the principal been replaced, but also most of my former teachers. The old principal (who had done so much for our school) had been relegated to teaching the third grade in grammar school in another county. His membership in the *Lidova strana* (a Catholic political party) was the reason for his and many other teachers' demotion. Fortunately for me, among the newcomers only the principal was a really dedicated member of the Communist Party.

I fitted easily into the routine of school work and very soon I realized that the Jesuits' training had helped me immensely because I was more advanced in my studies than my classmates. Of the twelve subjects I was taking, my report card at the end of school had only one "B" with "A's" in all the rest.

After the two-month summer vacation was over, I entered the ninth grade, the last year of junior high school. I realized in the very beginning that particular year would be a major stepping stone in my whole life, so I resolved to prepare for every single lesson very carefully.

The principal, Comrade Stika, was my physics and political education teacher, while Mr. Studeny taught me math. All other subjects were taught by the same teachers as in the previous year.

It soon became apparent that Comrade Stika was a very strict but a good teacher who explained everything very thoroughly. At the same time, I realized that I would have a difficult time satisfying him. He had not changed his opinion

37

of my being a "black sheep." In fact, I soon became more of an outcast in his eyes than ever, and I'm afraid it did not help matters much for my stand against him, especially when he spoke about the "imperialists" and particularly against the United States.

Once he said that all Americans are very poor, and that most of them are starving because of capitalism. He said, "Take the example of Mr. Fiala, who emigrated from here to the United States before World War II. He is working very hard as a garbage collector. It is necessary for him to work twelve hours a day, seven days a week. He has no Sundays off, no vacation, and still his family has to live in squalor. His family is compelled to pay very high rent and many times they have nothing to eat."

Where Comrade Stika dreamed up this story, I don't know. But he made the big mistake of using the name Fiala. By coincidence, he was talking about my mother's third cousin.

That time I was completely sure of my grounds, and I knew I could not let the opportunity to show him up go by. I raised my hand, and said, "Mister Stika, you must be mistaken about Mr. Fiala. He is not a garbage collector. He works in a factory; he does not work very hard. He has every Sunday off and even Saturdays are free days." (That was unheard of in my country.) "And he has a very nice, new house that has hot running water, a deep freeze, and even a T.V."

Comrade Stika fumed at my officiousness. He was not convinced even when I admitted that Mr. Fiala was a relative. So I promised to bring a picture my grandmother had got from Mr. Fiala only a few weeks before. At that particular time, a color photo was a real novelty to us, so the colored picture of Mr. Fiala and his wife and daughter, sitting in a comfortable living room scene, made quite an impression at school. The chairs in our homes were for utility more than for comfort, so the Fiala's furniture seemed very plush. Even their clothes looked exquisite. (Now that I am here in America, I realize what the photo showed was really an ordinary scene.) A second picture, with the family group posed in front of what seemed to us as an extraordinary house, left no room for doubt that Mr. Fiala had indeed done well for himself.

The principal was convinced, but he would not be outdone. He simply said he had mistakenly said Fiala when he really meant Kubena.

All the students knew it was a lie. He was trapped in his own propaganda—"Everything is good that serves Communism."

Things went smoothly enough in political science as long as Comrade Stika was speaking about facts and historical happenings. These things we could learn about and agree upon. It was when he spoke of our duties and slyly tried to inveigle the students, that there was dissension in the class.

"You young people," he would say, "are the future of the socialistic and communistic society. It is absolutely imperative that you understand where your place is. First of all, it is necessary for you to work in your homes to correct your parents' reactionary thinking. Try to convince them how nice it would be to give your farms, your machinery, your cattle to a collective commune and all work together . . ."

Most of my classmates were from farmers' families and the principal kept pounding away at this subject, hoping to find a weak spot and get through to them. He tried to convince us all that the *Kolchoz* and *Souchoz* (collective farming) style of work is much better than for each farmer to work separately.

Of course, my classmates did not agree with him. They had heard from their parents that the regime wanted to requisition all the land and all other property. Comrade Stika had a solution for the problem of parents who spoke against the regime in that manner. He often held up, as an example, a boy who lived in Russia and had reported to the authorities the "unpatriotic conduct" of his parents. For his "extra-

39

ordinary" deed, the boy was awarded a medal and was given prestige unequaled by his peers. He encouraged us to report any such "misconduct" of our parents to the proper authorities. He intimated that we, too, would be richly rewarded for our "patriotism" if we did so.

His explanation of the evolution of the true communistic society was outlined in four steps: people living under the slave yoke of capitalism must revolt against this slavery. From the chaos of this revolution would come a dictatorship of the proletariat.[1] As the people became more adept at self-government, the socialist state would evolve, and following this would be the (perfect) government of communism.

"Now we are in the era of the dictatorship of the proletariat. We must fight the bourgeois prejudices such as those found among your own parents. They are afraid to relinquish their property because they don't believe there can be a society without classes. But you, young people, are the vanguard of communism. We still have to evolve through socialism, but maybe some of you will be lucky enough to bask in pure communism.

"In communism there will be no rich, no poor, no bosses, no servants. Everyone will be equal. The man living under communism will not need to work. The work will be recreation. If he feels like working, he may, but there will be no necessity for work. In stores there will be plenty of merchandise for everyone. One can just go in and pick up what he wants without money.

"Imagine, boys and girls, there will be a dance in town. Every girl can go to the dress shop and choose the dress she likes without paying for it.

"There will be a real paradise on earth under communism."

"You said, Mr. Stika, there will not be a difference be-

---

1 Proletariat—one of the most common words in the communist vocabulary—means the working class which is striving to overthrow the old capitalistic system by revolution.

tween people. How can that be? What about the difference in personalities; what about the difference in one person being handsome while the other is not; one is physically strong, the other is not; one is healthy, the other is sick?" I questioned him.

I could see that my line of questioning irritated him, and, after a long reflection, he said, "Medicine will be so well developed that the doctors will be capable of curing every illness."

I didn't dare say aloud what I thought, "How ridiculous! The theory is very nice, but reality is very different."

I don't believe anyone believed the principal's theory—not even the principal himself. If fourteen and fifteen year-olds could see the fallacy of his communistic Utopia, certainly an intelligent man like Comrade Stika could not be that gullible. He was not a fool, but he was certainly mentally blinded because he did all he could to propagate communism.

The first semester in school went smoothly enough. Then, at mid-term, we were told that all ninth graders would have a public examination at the end of the school year. The examinations were to be given in Czech, Russian, and math, and each student could choose his fourth subject from among physics, chemistry, biology, history, or geography.

I chose physics because it was my favorite, and thanks to Comrade Stika, I was very good in it. In trying to belittle me in class, he had forced me to study harder than I would have ever done normally. I was determined he would not get the better of me.

I exerted all my efforts for the exam because I *had* to pass with high marks to be able to get into high school.

The school system in Czechoslovakia is set up differently than it is in America. All children are required to attend school through the ninth grade. Then, only a very small number of students continue on to high school. Only those from this small group can ever hope to become professional men and women. From my class of forty-five students, there were only three who went to high school that year. So if a student is really interested in higher education, it is imperative that he be accepted by a high school, and that acceptance is not easy. The high schools themselves are different, too. First, there is the usual high school called gymnasium (recently *jedenacti* or *dvanactiletka*) that is the most popular and has the broadest curriculum. The Bishop's school was of this type. It is a kind of liberal arts school from where the student can go to the university to become a doctor of either medicine or philosophy, or to become an engineer of either agriculture, chemistry or mechanics.

The second type of high school is a technical school called a *prumyslovka,* in which a student prepares to be an engineer of mechanics, electronics, or chemistry, exclusively.

If a student wants to prepare for business, he goes to an *obchodni skola* or business school.

If his choice is medicine, either as a doctor or nurse, he attends a *zdravotni skola* or medical school.

In that way the schools are highly specialized in their training for the chosen vocations. Of course, since each town is unable to maintain four different high schools, the student must commute to or live in the town which has the type of high school he attends.

Shortly after the announcement of the public examination, we were told that all ninth graders must choose their life's vocation by the end of the school year.

For those who wanted to stay at home and work on the farms with their parents, or for those who wanted to work in the factories as helpers, there was no problem. But for those of us who wanted to go to high school, it was a major decision because whatever type of high school we attended determined our profession, or whatever profession we chose, we had to be accepted by that type of high school.

Since I had not given my life's vocation too much thought after I returned from the Bishop's school, it was most difficult

42

for me to make the decision of the choice of the high school.

The fact that I had to decide upon my future life came too quickly. I was not ready to make such a decision—not yet. That's why I took an application for the gymnasium from where I had a choice of a wider range of professions and three more years to make my final decision. I was confident that I would be accepted at the gymnasium, because my grades were the best in the class and I had been careful not to give any teacher a chance to question my conduct.

One morning, later in the semester, I was surprised when Mr. Hubalik, one of my teachers, came to me and said, "Peter, the principal would like to talk with you and Marka."

"Immediately?" I asked.

"Yes. Find Marka and go to see him right away."

I was not prepared for bad news, but I was certainly curious as to what he could want. I wasn't aware of any infraction of the rules.

"What could he possibly want?" I kept asking myself as I looked for Marka.

I found her sitting at her desk, reviewing her history lesson for the last time. She was one of the best students in the class and very conscientious about each lesson.

"Marka, Mr. Hubalik told me that you and I are to report to Comrade Stika in his office."

"Right now? Wait a few minutes. I want to finish reviewing for history. I'm not sure I know today's lesson very well."

"Look, Marka, we won't be here for history anyway if we have to go to Comrade Stika's office. Mr. Hubalik said we should go immediately, so come on."

Reluctantly she left her desk. "Do you know what Comrade Stika wants?"

"I have no idea."

We found Comrade Stika sitting at his desk.

He looked up at us and said, "I have something very important to tell you." Picking up some papers that we recognized as application forms for high school, he continued,

"Your applications for high school were not accepted. You probably know the reasons we had to reject them, don't you?"

"No, I certainly do not," I said, trying to control my voice.

"Very well, I'll tell you," Comrade Stika said, looking intently at me with his pale blue eyes. It was a look that haunts me to this very day. He seemed to be gloating over his position and the authority it commanded.

"You, Peter, did not get permission to go to the gymnasium because of your father's political activity in *Lidova strana,* and also because of your family's religious convictions. Your being in the Bishop's high school is also a big obstacle. We just can't trust people like you. We risk letting you go to school, and giving you an education and position in society only to have you work against the Communist Party and the working class. No. We simply can't afford it. Like a treacherous dog, you may bite the hand that feeds you."

Turning to Marka, he said in a venomous tone, "And you, Marka, can't go to the gymnasium because of your brother's activities."

Marka's oldest brother had been a teacher before the communists had come to power. He and Comrade Stika had been colleagues, but had severed their friendship over their political allegiances. While Comrade Stika tried to reeducate youth in Marx-Leninist ideas, Marka's brother was having far greater success as a Catholic Boy Scout leader. He had almost all the boys active in Boy Scouts and was accomplishing a great deal of good, while Comrade Stika had only a few followers and very little activity.

Comrade Stika had never forgiven his former friend and evidently had bided his time to strike against him. This was the perfect time. Comrade Stika had power and he could use it for his personal vengeance.

"That's all I wanted to tell you," he said curtly. "Here are new application forms. Check with your home-room teacher to see where you can apply for a job. After this year, you cannot go to school anymore."

I went home very dejected that afternoon. I had such great ambitions for my life. I had really wanted to *invest* my life —not just *spend* it. My father had taught me that the only way to accomplish the most good in life is to prepare a solid foundation with a good education. Now that dream was burst as though it were a bubble.

I walked into the kitchen where my mother was feeding my baby brother, Frantik, his supper. My father had not come home from the factory yet. I was glad to be able to tell Mother first, so that she could help me break the news to him. I knew he would be crushed. Ever since I was born, he had planned that the big things he hoped to provide for me in life would be a good home with a religious background and a good education. He felt that with these essentials as a bulwark, I could meet any of life's challenges. He was determined to give me all the opportunities to continue school. He knew it would not be easy for him to support me for so many years under the existing economic conditions, but he was ready and willing—even eager—to sacrifice anything just to give me a chance.

Mother was upset, but not shaken, at the news. She showed her usual composure. In retrospect, she was probably very much hurt at the news, but would not let her true feelings show because she knew how disappointed I was and she wanted to spare my feelings as much as possible.

"Don't worry too much, Peta," she blandly reassured. "Father will find some way for you to go high school."

Her words did console me somewhat. I had always thought of my father as a real hero, and hearing the confidence Mother also had in him helped.

We heard the door close and Father came in calling his usual greeting. *"Pochvalen bud Jezis Kristus. Je nekdo doma?"* (Praised be Jesus Christ. Is someone at home?). He walked into the kitchen and exclaimed, "What's the matter here? You look as though you've lost your best friend, Peta."

"Father, I can't go to high school," I blurted.

"Who said so?" he demanded.

"Comrade Stika. He called me and Marka into his office today . . ." Then I related the whole story.

Father's reaction was completely different from Mother's. He had planned so completely on my going to high school, that he had more or less taken it for granted that I would go.

"I'll go see about *that*," he roared. "Since when is faith in God and membership in *Lidova strana* a crime? Come on, Peta, we're going to get this straight right now."

"First eat your supper, and then you can go," Mother entreated.

"Supper can wait. Peta's future is more important. Anyway, I'm not hungry."

We stormed directly into the principal's office.

"Mr. Stika, my son tells me that his application for high school was not accepted."

"That's true. And I told him why."

"Do you think the reasons you gave are obstacles big enough to stop my son's education?"

"They certainly are."

"Just where is the law that makes it a crime to believe in God or to belong to *Lidova strana?* It is just the opposite. Our constitution explicitly assures us of religious freedom."

"That's right, Mr. Esterka, but you forgot one thing. We are living in the dictatorship of the proletariat and we cannot let your son go to school because he and you are enemies of the working class."

"What do you mean 'enemies of the working class'? I have been working in the factory as an ordinary worker practically my entire life. Am I not a member of the working class myself? How can you say I am its enemy?"

Comrade Stika retorted, "Neither you nor any of the members of your family, your father and all your brothers, are in the Communist Party. Furthermore, you probably *never* will become even favorable to us."

"Is being a member of the Communist Party a condition

46

for being able to go to high school? Is there no consideration for knowledge or capability to become a sincere and dedicated citizen of our nation and work for the good of society?"

Comrade Stika ignored the question. "Look, Mr. Esterka," he said very vehemently, "we cannot be sure that we will be able to re-educate your son to become a true communist. Therefore, as I told him this afternoon: 'we will not feed a treacherous dog and then have him bite the hand that feeds him.' He could hurt us much more severely if he were educated than he could as an ordinary worker. I'll never let him go to high school. That's my final word."

5. FUTILE EFFORTS

School life went on as usual. I spent a lot of time and effort studying for the examinations that were soon to follow. After our interview with Comrade Stika, my father had advised me to try to remain the best student in the class. "Not because of some kind of foolish pride," he explained, "but because, when Comrade Stika sees that you are really trying, he may relent and let you go on to school. After all, he is a good teacher and if he sees that you really want to learn and are truly intelligent, he will want to see that intelligence nourished and grow."

How little my father knew of the blindness of Comrade Stika!

"You do the best you can, Peta, and I will talk with the factory's union director. He is a good friend of mine. I'm sure he will help me if he possibly can," Father assured me.

So my father went to see the director of his union at the factory, Ruda Prikryl. For many years they had worked together in the same department. The director listened sympathetically and promised to help.

Mr. Prikryl had been a member of the Communist Party practically all his life. He sincerely believed in the communist doctrine that only communism could solve the social problems in the world and he worked ardently for that ideal.

After the Communists took over in 1948, he could have got a very important and well paid job because of his long standing affiliation with the party. But he refused the offer saying, "I have always been only a worker; I learned my job and did it well. I never learned to use a pen, so why should I take a job that I am not capable of doing? Give it to someone who knows how to do those things."

48

He continued working for the Party, spending his free time going from meeting to meeting and promoting the Party's aims. Finally, he was elected to the post of director of the union in the factory where he worked. At first he wanted to refuse that position also, but his co-workers convinced him that he could do much good for them in that capacity. He really tried to do his best for everyone. That's why he tried to help me.

Another reason he tried to help me was to repay an old debt to my father. During the war, he lived in town where there was often not enough food, especially during 1943-45. The people who lived in the towns were often hungry. Food commodities were scarce and it was commonplace for towns-people to trade clothes, silver, carpets, table-ware, glass-ware —anything they had—to farmers for flour, butter, meat, or other farm goods.

Mr. Prikryl's family was not rich and they did not have such things to trade so their plight was often desperate. My father was working at the same machine with Mr. Prikryl at that time, and knew of his distress. Father felt sorry for him and tried to help him find foodstuff that he could afford to buy with what little money he had.

At the time I needed his help, he was willing to do what-ever he could for me even though my father and he were divided over their political ideals.

His efforts had favorable results. A few days after he promised he would help, he came to my father and said, "Pavel, we were talking about your son. After a big argument, I got permission for him to continue his studies, but only in a technical or business school. You can understand why. They are afraid that if they let him go to the gymnasium, he could later become a priest."

"Thanks, Ruda, I understand. I would like to see Peta go to the gymnasium, but I know this is the best you can do, and I appreciate your efforts."

"Try to find a school for him outside this county," suggested Mr. Prikryl. "Out of sight, out of mind, you know. And to stay out of public view is very important."

"I understand," replied my father.

That evening Father came home with a big broad smile on his face and the good news. "You have permission to continue your studies, Peta. You may go to either the technical or the business school."

I decided to go to technical school rather than business school.

So I would be an engineer. There was no other choice if I went to *prumyslovka* (the technical school). This was not what I really wanted, but I was satisfied. My father had done his best. I realized it and was grateful.

I was accepted by the school in Breclav. I immediately liked the principal, who was very pleasant to me when I arrived, and showed him my report card.

"You are welcome in our school. We are always glad to have good students. I only hope you will continue in the same way in our school."

"I will do my best," I assured him.

"Good. Consider yourself one of our new students."

I was surprised the principal didn't mention my *cadre card.*[2] Later we learned that he was not a member of the Communist Party, and did not care to get involved in politics. I felt confident that I was accepted by the school and began to contemplate being an engineer. Little did I know that I was only building castles in the air.

---

2 The cadre card is the name given to the file that the communists keep on each and every citizen in order that they may see who their sympathizers and adversaries are. It contains every shred of information that they can learn about each person. Besides vital information such as date of birth, occupation etc., there are such things as whether one goes to church; what remarks one makes at work about the conditions in the nation; what one's opinions are on every subject that one might have spoken about; what one's attitude is; and whatever other details can be found out.

Only a short time after my Father and I visited the principal in Breclav, I received a short note from him saying, "After checking your record, I regret to inform you that you are not accepted by our school."

"That is impossible. He plainly said that you are accepted," my father lamented when he read the note. "It must be a mistake. I will go to see him personally and clear up this matter."

"I'm sorry, Mr. Esterka," the principal told my father. "There's nothing I can do for your son. I told you that your son was accepted but 'they' said *'absolutely no'*."

He wouldn't say who "they" were, so Father went to see Mr. Prikryl who was able to pinpoint "they" as being Comrade Stika.

True to his word, Comrade Stika was determined I would never go to high school.

Just a short time before the public examination, we had what we called our school's "Olympics." The "Olympics" were part of our Physical Education class—a sort of exhibition of our accomplishments.

The events of the program consisted of the 60 meter dash, high jump, broad jump, discus and javelin throwing. I was overjoyed with the outcome. In the 60 meter dash, I won first place with a time of 7. 7 seconds. I also won first place in the broadjump and the discus throwing. I placed second in the high jump. The whole class made a very good showing and our Physical Education teacher, Mr. Kral, was so pleased with the results of our "Olympics" that he playfully challenged the three best athletes to run the 60 meter dash against him. He said he was quite good in this event and wanted to race us. I had gained a great deal of confidence from the events I had just won and was ready to compete against any taker.

We lined up at the starting line. I was very nervous competing against the teacher because he was much taller and stronger than I. I knew from soccer that one of the other boys was also very fast. But I wanted to win that race very badly.

"Get on your mark," called Comrade Stika, who was the judge of the race. He was very interested in sports since he had been a P. E. teacher himself in his younger days.

"Get set."

"Go."

I ran as fast as I could. There was a lot of excitement from the sidelines. Everyone was yelling and cheering their choice to the finish line. I realized no one was in front of me. I exerted my full capacity.

I crossed the finish line.

I *won.*

My time was even better than before—7.6 seconds.

The P.E. teacher came up smiling and shook my hand. "It is a marvelous time, Peter."

Comrade Stika looked amazed and rechecked his watch. He said disdainfully, "In Zlin's High School, Holubec ran it even better. He ran the 60 meter in 7.4 seconds."

"Yes, but he was much older than Peter is. And Peter ran in tennis shoes and on this inferior track. I also know Holubec. Once he even ran it in 7.3 seconds, but he was wearing track shoes and on Zlin's official track. That makes a lot of difference," said Mr. Kral.

Later, when he and I were alone, he asked me, "What do you intend to do after you are finished here? Wouldn't you like to join *Tyrsuv ustav?*" *Tyrsuv ustav* is a school for athletes and coaches that specializes in body development and training in physical skills. It has some degree of academic accreditation.

"I would like to go to high school. That's the most important thing to me, but Comrade Stika won't permit it."

Maybe it was because I was his pupil and he had trained me and wanted to see me make the most of his training. Whatever the reason, Mr. Kral was still enthusiastic.

"I'll write to the director of *Tyrsuv ustav* about you," he promised. "There's no doubt about it, your time on the 60 meter dash was marvelous. Maybe you could some day represent Czechoslovakia in the dash in international competition, or at least, you would be a good P. E. teacher."

His enthusiasm made me feel very good. But when I told my father what the teacher had said, he was a little disappointed.

"You must try to do something more substantial than playing sports all your life," he advised.

I understood what he meant. I knew Father never placed much emphasis on sports even though he enjoyed a game of soccer as much as almost anyone. But we both knew that athletics was not what either of us wanted for me in life.

Mr. Kral tried to have me accepted by the *Tyrsuv ustav*, but again Comrade Stika blocked my admission. Because of my *cadre card*, it would always ultimately be his refusal to give a recommendation that would keep me from any school or job.

Once again he called me to his office and told me quite explicitly, "Quit trying to be accepted by any school. I've already told you that I'll never give you permission. And I've told you why. You know that all schools have to ask to see your *cadre card* and I will never change my mind. Is that clear?"

I was almost despondent by the cold fact that all school doors were locked and barred to me. Desperately I thought, "What kind of a fool am I? Why did I ever try to be an honor student? I could have been out enjoying myself, playing soccer, instead of always rushing home to do my homework. Why didn't I do like other boys?"

All my hopes were gone and I was desperate. My whole future seemed to hang by a thread. It was as though I were a puppet and Comrade Stika was the puppeteer. My very fibre rebelled at the thought of my life being manipulated by a man of such vindictive callousness.

"Don't take it so hard, Peter. Losing one year in school is not the end of the world," my Uncle Jirka tried to encourage me. "Look at me, I lost not one but four years during the

53

Nazi occupation, and still I achieved my goal. You have time —plenty of time. Try looking at it this way; one year in the factory could be one of the best and most useful experiences of your life. After you've worked awhile, you will be able to see life in a new perspective and you will mature earlier. Then you will be able to study for more than good grades— you will study for your life's ambition. The Americans will come very soon. And then next year you will go to school. I'm sure you will. You will see. Next year you will go to school."

I believed my Uncle Jirka because he was a most intelligent and admirable man. When the Nazis closed Karlova (Charles) University in Prague on November 17, 1939 (after shooting some of the Czech students and arresting others), Uncle Jirka was among those arrested and sent to a Nazi concentration camp. Upon his release after the war was over, he finished his studies and became an engineer, and later earned his doctorate in science. Because his main interest was people, he didn't confine his work to the laboratory. He spent most of his free time working with youth, and became one of the top leaders of Catholic youth in Moravia.

Several youth leaders fled the country when the communists took over in February, 1948, but he stayed. "Someone has to stay to be able to lead the way when the communists are overthrown," he explained when asked why he didn't escape.

The communists arrested Uncle Jirka for his activity with the youth. His "crime" had been teaching youngsters how to be useful in building their own futures, their families, and their nation after the Nazi occupation, but his methods did not conform with the communists' ideas. So he was imprisoned again.

After serving a term of almost five years, he was released by the communists and sent, as an ordinary worker, back to the factory in which, before his arrest, he had been the head of the laboratory. Later he was allowed to return to the

54

laboratory, but not in the capacity he had left it. They must have needed him desperately to let him return. During his absence, three engineers filled his place in the laboratory. When he came back, he was put under the constant scrutiny of a Russian engineer. Only then was he allowed to continue his work.

In spite of all his difficulties, Uncle Jirka was still an optimist. He firmly believed that the Americans would come to liberate us. We *had* to believe it in order to sustain ourselves after the all-too-recent, brutal domination of the Nazis. To know that another reign of terror was upon us was more than we felt we could endure. The arrival of the Americans was the hope of my nation—the sole consolation in those days. That one hope kept many from despair, suicide, or insanity.

I was young and ambitious, and realized that some of my friends, who were no more qualified than I, would become engineers, doctors, teachers or at least have some kind of a substantial future, while I would spend my life being disparaged. It was the price I had to pay for my religious convictions and personal integrity. Certainly I could have yielded and become a communist. That would have simplified everything. But to betray every ideal I had, I would not—could not—do.

So I, too, started to believe and hope with others that: "The Americans will come very soon. They will liberate us and all other people suffering under the communist dictatorship."

Then I would get a chance to go to school.

It was only that hope which gave me enough perseverance to continue my studies diligently for the approaching examinations.

Even though I excelled in both the written and oral examinations and finished junior high with honors, nothing was changed. As far as Comrade Stika was concerned, my school days were over.

And his decision was irrevocable.

55

6. THE INTERNAT

The fact that I could not go to high school as long as the communists were in power was a bitter disappointment to me. I realized that they could destroy me any time if it pleased them, but still my ambitions were not subdued. Instead, it became a kind of challenge to me. I was young enough and cursed enough to have a lot of spunk, and I was eager to struggle for even a little freedom—or maybe it was a fight for my emerging manhood itself.

"O.K.," I determinedly told myself. "It looks as though I cannot go to high school or any school this year. I have to do something. But what? I've got to go someplace where I can learn something and where I'll not just waste time, because someday, I *will* be something."

After inquiring about existing possibilities, the director of an electrical company promised me that if I would apply myself well, perhaps after a year or two, I might possibly go to a technical school. His company needed skilled technicians to work on sensitive electrical equipment. To get the necessary training for the job he had in mind, I had to go to an *internat*.

An *internat* is a sort of boarding school in which the apprentices live and are trained for different types of jobs, depending on the type of *internat* they attend. Actually, their main purpose is to take young people away from the influence of the home and family and indoctrinate them in communism. It was definitely not the type of school I wanted to attend, but it was necessary for me to get some sort of job. My parents and I signed a two-year contract that bound me to an electrician's *internat*.

So, in September, I left for the *internat* in Prerov. The school and workshop were located in the town, while the *internat*

56

itself was in a castle about 10 or 12 kilometers (about 7 miles) from the town. Although the castle had been renovated to accommodate the apprentices' and instructors' needs, it was still a magnificent place surrounded by beautiful formal gardens. The castle had two wings—in the left one were the boys' dormitories and in the right wing were the girls' dormitories. The front section was used for offices, recreation rooms, and instructors' bedrooms.

The time schedule was much like that of the Bishop's high school or any other boarding school, so I quickly adjusted to *internat* life. But the thing that I found impossible to accept was the communist indoctrination that we were made to listen to for an hour each day. But even more insidious to the vulnerable boys and girls was the complete withdrawal of family ties and religious principles.

Shortly after we arrived, the second year apprentices returned to the *internat* from their vacation. I was appalled to see how completely lax most of them were in regard to their religious duties. They, too, had just recently come from ordinary homes, not unlike homes we had just left. But the *internat's* athletic influence was apparent to their outlook on life, proving how adept the communists were in perverting young minds. But still, there were a few whom even the stealthy communists could not break.

One such boy was among the old group. He was called Tonda, which is the nickname for Antonin. He was from an extremely wealthy family that had maids, a car, and even a chauffeur. Wealth to that extent was extremely rare in my country. He and his family lived in almost another world from the work-a-day world we knew. His parents were aristocrats who were well known in international society. They spoke several languages and were familiar with the French and Italian Riviera and all the prominent art galleries and theaters of Europe.

One night, the communists confiscated everything Tonda's family owned. His mother was forced to take a job as an

57

assistant librarian, while his father, who was a distinguished professor at the university, fled to the Near East.

"Imagine, one day I had everything I could possibly want, and the next morning I awoke to find myself in worse condition than a beggar," his mother once told me. "One day my son went to school in a car accompanied by his governess, and the next day he had to walk because I didn't even have money for a streetcar."

In the length of a day, her residence was reduced from a mansion to one shabby room in an old tenement house. Her fairy-tale existence and influential friends were gone forever. But she remained steadfast in spite of her tragedy. "I have one thing they can never steal from me. That's my faith in God. And it is the only thing that keeps me alive."

Life was hard, at best, for the people who had never known anything but privation, but for a lady of such elegant tastes, it must have been almost unbearable.

Tonda, like his mother, was flung into a world of reality with which he was not prepared to cope. And yet, he, too, shared his mother's faith. Whenever I began to think that my future seemed hopeless, I would wonder how he must have felt.

The first Sunday we were at the *internat,* an all-day hike was planned for us. I was concerned that there was no time allotted for Mass, so I went to the director to ask permission to go to Mass.

"We do not have Mass on the schedule," said Comrade Ryba, the director.

"But I'm a Catholic and it is my duty to go. When I signed the contract to come here, I was promised that I would be given a chance to go to Mass each Sunday and all holydays," I explained.

"Of course, you must realize that you are under my direction now, Comrade . . . ," he paused, waiting for me to introduce myself.

"Esterka, sir."

58

"Here we call each other Comrade, Comrade Esterka."

"But I'm not a member of the Communist Party, sir."

"Yes, I know you are not, but you are a member of the C. S. M. (*Ceskoslovensky Svaz Mladeze*) aren't you?"

Ceskoslovensky Svaz Mladeze is a young people's organization of the Communist Party for youth from fifteen to twenty-five.

"No, sir. I'm not."

"Surely you belong to the *Pionyr*" (a Communist organization for children from grammar school age to fifteen).

"No, sir. I don't."

"Then you had better join the C. S. M., Comrade Esterka," he advised me. Then he added, "To show you that I am a reasonable man, I'll give you permission to go to Mass on Sunday, provided you find at least ten others who also want to go. That is all. *Cest Praci* (honor the work), Comrade."

I could not bring myself to utter this Communistic phrase of greeting. It was a symbol of everything that was repulsive to me. The words *Cest Praci* (honor the work) stuck in my throat. To address anyone as "Comrade" was also repulsive to me, but it was in such common usage, that some of its repugnance was diminished.

I went directly to the boys and asked how many wanted to go to Mass on Sunday. In just a few minutes I had more than fifteen signatures, including one Protestant boy, who signed up to go to Mass because he was not allowed to attend services in his church. Only three boys refused to sign up for Mass.

Then I went to the girls and immediately all but one of them signed up.

So the next Sunday, four apprentices went on the hike and the rest of us went to church accompanied by a lady instructor.

The next three Sundays, the attendance at Mass was also good. So Comrade Ryba decided to use a new approach.

He announced a free bus trip to Gottwaldov to see a cham-

59

pionship soccer game for the following Sunday. The trip was
timed so that attendance at Mass was out of the question.
Naturally, it was a big temptation for all of us, but still some
did not go on the trip, but went to Mass instead.

That was a blow to Comrade Ryba's prestige and he would
not forget that I was the one who was behind the whole affair.
Soon I felt his subtle wrath.

Not long afterwards, it was my turn to lead morning calisthenics. I was confident that I could lead them very well.
When we were finished, Comrade Ryba called me to him.

"Comrade Esterka, how long did you prepare to lead the
calisthenics?"

"Oh, I don't know, sir. Probably three or four minutes."
I still called him "Sir;" I made an effort to avoid the use of
that hated word "Comrade."

"That's not enough. You will have to prepare them much
better the next time. I'm not at all satisfied with you."

I was very hurt at his reprimand—much more than I realized that anything that trivial could hurt me. Perhaps I was
too proud of my physical accomplishments, but deep inside
I felt sure I had done well and he was goading me.

There were other ways, too, in which Comrade Ryba tried
to make life difficult for me. Once it was because I didn't
have my bed made well enough. Other times it was other
things; things that of themselves were insignificant, but they
were so continual that they could not have been accidental.

One insignificant thing that grew all out of proportion was
a tiny gold cross I wore on the lapel of my coat. It was the
custom for all the boys from the vicinity in which I grew up
to wear those crosses. It seemed that even that small act of
faith could not be tolerated by Comrade Ryba. He called me
into his office.

"Good afternoon, sir," I said as I entered.

"Cest Praci (honor the work)," he snapped.

"I've told you before, Comrade Esterka, that we say '*Cest*

Praci' instead of the bourgeois greeting. And we address each other as Comrade. Do you understand?"

"But I don't belong to the C. S. M. and I understand that only the members of the Communist Party and C. S. M. are supposed to use this terminology."

"Yes, that's right. But you, our youth, are the future members of the Communist Party. Even you, Comrade Esterka, will be a communist someday, and then you will be ashamed of today's behavior. Be sensible. Wise up before you ruin your future. You are an intelligent boy. It is only your family and the atmosphere in which you were educated that are not healthy for you. Now you are far away from home and your parents. Nobody knows you around here. Go ahead and join the C.S.M.," he tempted, "and work among the others. Try to realize the scope of what is going on in Czechoslovakia today. And remember this one thing: you can't swim against the tide. I, myself, joined the Party only after February, 1948. I realized it was the necessary thing to do if I wanted to live a successful life."

So that was it! Comrade Ryba was one of the so-called "After February Communists." Among the people, those who joined the Party after February, 1948 were known as *Prospechari*.

These were ambitious men who were afraid for their own positions. They had joined the Party for their own selfish reasons instead of for their political convictions. In a way they were despicable men who knew they had power only as long as they were useful to the Party. So they worked hard in order that there would be no question of their loyalty. Soon many of them were top ranking men with real influence, sometimes having the power of small dictators in towns, schools, factories, or counties.

The old faithful members of the Party had clean slates with nothing to hide, so they could ask for small favors from the Party, but these *Prospechari* had to be very, very careful, and show that they were willing to serve. Therefore, they were most harsh on the "non-conformists." In some cases these "johnny-come-latelies," in their grab for power, even purged the old members from the Party.

The lesser *Prospechari* followed their orders from Prague most zealously; the leaders in Prague, in turn, were most scrupulous to follow their orders from Moscow; and at that time, all major orders came directly from Stalin and Moscow.

"The reason I called you in, Comrade Esterka, is the small cross on your coat. Don't you think it is a provocation?" Comrade Ryba asked.

"I don't see anything wrong with wearing it."

"But I do. It is forbidden to wear the badge of a political party in which you are not a member."

"It is not the badge of any political party," I declared.

"Yes it is and you know it. It is the badge of the *Lidova strana*," Comrade Ryba asserted, and I couldn't convince him that it was not, even though it really was not. The cross must have bothered him became he certainly did not want to see me wear it.

Finally he said, "All right, Comrade Esterka, do as you wish. Your future is in your own hands. But you can be sure about one thing: I learned from your *cadre card* that you wish to go to school. I'll not let you go—at least not next year. First you have to show me that you are trying to be a 'new man,' a man of the communist society who doesn't believe what Grandpa or Grandma told him. Don't you know they were living under the clerical darkness—under the influence of priest? But you are living in a different world, a modern world, where we no longer believe what the priests taught us. We want to be a new, modern, educated people. We find our knowledge in the discoveries of science and not in the fables they told us in catechism. This is my final decision: join the C. S. M., then we will be friends and I'll be glad to erase from your *cadre card* the facts that you don't want to call the others 'Comrade;' that you don't want to say *'Cest Praci'* (honor the work); and that you wear the cross

62

on your coat. All this will be forgotten the moment you will become a 'new man,'" he said very determinedly.

"And remember one more thing, Comrade Esterka," he added trying to be helpful and understanding, "there is the old Czech axiom: 'You can't pierce the wall with your head.'"

So to become Comrade Ryba's friend was not so difficult after all. At least, it did not seem hard to him. But for me it was impossible to accept such a "friendship." There was not only the question of collaborating with the communists; there also had to be a betrayal of parents, friends, the priests who I knew were suffering in concentration camps, and most of all, a betrayal of God Himself. No, I could not do it. No career was worth *that* price.

"Convince me that God doesn't exist. Then I can become a 'new man' as you suggested," I hedged.

"O.K. I will. But not today. Today I don't have time."

I knew that lack of time was not the real reason Comrade Ryba had for not trying to convince me because turning young minds in favor of communism was the prime reason for having the *internats* in the first place. First he needed to read some communist pamphlet on how to persuade a young person to accept atheism. I couldn't help but wonder what argument he would use to disprove the existence of God when He has gone to such lengths to show Himself everywhere.

That night I wrote a letter to my family telling them of the day's happenings and my conversation with Comrade Ryba.

Within a few days, my mother came for what she said was a casual visit. But the moment I saw her, I knew her visit was not casual at all. After she warmly greeted me, she said, "Peta, you are going home with me."

"I don't know if they will let me."

"They will," she said quite firmly.

I was surprised to see Mother so positive that I would be going home with her. She was most determined, so I didn't say any more.

"Mr. Ryba, I am taking my son home with me," Mother said as we walked into his office.

"Just a minute, Mrs. Esterka," he exclaimed, trying to silence Mother. "It is not as simple as that. Did you forget that you signed the contract for your son to stay here for two years? He is now my responsibility."

"He is still my son, Mr. Ryba, and if I say he will go home with me, I mean it, and he will go."

"Then you will be in trouble."

"Not after what I saw in the park coming here. If someone will be in trouble, then it will be you, Mr. Ryba. Because, just as you said, you are responsible for our children, and what I saw just a few minutes ago, is not a very good sign that you are capable of taking care of our children."

It was clear that he didn't know how to handle a woman of Mother's disposition. He didn't know what she meant exactly.

"Tell me, Mrs. Esterka, what did you see in the park?"

"Go see for yourself. There are boys and girls together; the girls are wearing short shorts and sitting on the laps of the boys . . ."

Comrade Ryba interrupted her, "That's nothing bad. I thought you saw them trying to hang someone." His tone dripped with sarcasm. "You must understand that young people today are different than you were. And for girls and boys to mingle together like that is good for them. They will get accustomed to each other and there will not be any more problems and curiosity among them."

"That's just great! I'm glad you yourself told me this. At least now I know what kind of hands the children are in."

"They are not children any more, Mrs. Esterka."

"Yes, they are to me!" Mother said emphatically. "And now I'm telling you, I'm taking my son with me."

"You will be in trouble, Mrs. Esterka. Peter has stayed here almost one month and you will have to pay for him."

"All right, so I'll pay."

64

"It is not as easy as you may think. You will have to pay for each day he has been here. And the price will not be small if you insist on taking him. It would be unwise on your part since your husband is not a wealthy man."

"We'll discuss this later, Mr. Ryba. Goodbye." Mother turned to me and said, "Peta, go pack your things. I'll wait for you in the corridor."

On our way home, we stopped in Prerov at the central office of the *internat*. Mother explained the whole situation and told them that she was taking me home with her.

7. DISCOURSE

The next day after I returned home from Prerov, I went with Father to his factory in Zamky to try to get a job. Father worked in a plywood factory that was located in Zamky, which is about four and a half miles from our home in Hradsko. He commuted each day by bus.

The foreman said he had plenty of work for me and immediately took me to a sawing machine and explained how to operate it.

"After this shift is over, come to the personnel office and fill out the forms. I'll go now and tell them that I've hired you," said the foreman.

So I became a wage earner. But not for long. It was probably one of the shortest employments on their records. About ten o'clock, the foreman returned and said, "I'm sorry, but I can't let you work here. Go to the personnel office. They want to talk with you."

In the personnel office, Mr. Prikryl, the head of the union, was waiting with a clerk. On the walls of the office were charts with production graphs and posters on which were written communistic slogans.

"Comrade Esterka, we got a notice from the employment office saying we could not hire you in the factory," said the clerk.

"Why not? Is there some reason?"

"Yes, there is. You were in the *internat*, weren't you?"

"Yes, sir, I was."

"And you escaped from there?" he inquired.

"I left the *internat*," I admitted.

"I don't wish to interrogate you as to the reasons you left.

66

I just wanted to tell you that you can't work in our factory or in any other factory. You *have* to go to an *internat*."

"How is it that I *have* to go there?"

"Peta, please, sit down and wait for me while I get your father so we can come to a clear understanding about this," Mr. Prikryl said. The clerk left with him and in a little while, only Mr. Prikryl returned with my father.

"Let me explain what is going on, Pavel," he said to my father, as they sat down. "The whole problem is that Comrade Stika wants Peta in the *internat*. He brought it up again last night at the Party Secretariat. He said that Peta is a smart boy, but too dangerous for our society and he suggested that we at least try to indoctrinate him. He also said the best way for such indoctrination is for him to be in an *internat* where he is far away from his family's influence and under the guidance of a communist tutor. The other Comrades agreed with Comrade Stika's suggestion, and so I'm afraid Peta has to go to some *internat*. Just in case you will not let him go, he can't get a job anywhere. Then you will have to pay for every day he stayed in the *internat* in Prerov. They will set the price exeedingly high. You cannot afford to pay such a 'ransom' for your son. I wanted you to know what was decided at the meeting last night," Mr. Prikryl ended sadly.

"Maybe it would be a good idea for Peta to stay at home one year," my father seemed to be thinking aloud. "Then it will be much easier for him to go to school." (In order to change one's classification in a communist country, it is always necessary to get permission from one's superiors. Father was thinking that if I would not have a classification either as a student or a worker, then I would not need permission to go to school.)

"I don't agree with you," said Mr. Prikryl. "I think that if Peta does not go to the *internat,* the doors of every kind of school will be closed to him permanently."

"Ruda, where is all this freedom under the government of the working people that you are always talking and dreaming

67

of, when a worker's son can't even go to school?" Father was getting vehement.

"Don't get angry, Pavel. It is not our fault. First you have to understand that right now we are in the transitory state of the dictatorship of the proletariat. We have to fight the capitalists and bourgeois and all their influences that are ingrained in the people."

"What does Peta know about capitalists?" Father asked exasperatedly.

"Probably nothing. But he has many wrong ideas because of your influences."

"What do you mean 'wrong ideas'? Is it something bad not to be a communist?"

"You know, Pavel, that when a forest is cleared, even some of the saplings are not spared."

"Don't tell me that it is an accident that so many innocent people must suffer these days. And for what? For a better life for the working people? Look around us. Is there any improvement in our condition since the communists took over?"

"We have everything in our hands to better ourselves."

"Do you really believe that, Ruda? Who are 'we'? You are one of them, and you have worked so hard for so long. And yet, what kind of power do *you* have? Sure, you are now in office . . . "

"I didn't want to be there," Mr. Prikryl defended himself.

"I know that, and I don't intend to reproach *you*. I know that you are doing the best you can and I appreciate the efforts you are making for the men in this factory. But even though you are in office, you, like the rest of us workers, are in the same situation as we all were under the capitalists— even worse. The capitalists didn't chase us from one meeting to another. At Christmas they gave us a bonus. We worked forty-eight hours and nobody bothered us with *brigadas*[3] on

---

3 Brigadas are "voluntary obligatory" work that is done when and where it is needed. There is no pay for this work and all students, soldiers, and workers are required to perform it.

Sundays and after work. No one forced us to pay for Korea.[4]

"And what happened when the working class came to power? Let me tell you. We never starved as much then, as we are starving today. Even those of you who are communists and are at the trough, don't feel the comforts you claim to be offering to the working class.

"What happened to your dreams of there being an equal society with no classes? Open your eyes, man. Is there really equality for everyone? We have the same social classes again. It's true that the capitalists don't exploit us any more today. The Party has seen to that all right, because you have destroyed the capitalists and all that they had. But still we are exploited more than before. Who is doing it now? You know who, but won't admit it. It is simply those who took the capitalists' place—those who try to convince us that they care about us, but, in fact, they are worse than the capitalists ever were.

"Of course, we could argue here all day without result, because you are just blind enough not to see the facts and the reality," Father affirmed.

"No, Pavel, I'm not blind. I see it, but what can we do about it?" Mr. Prikryl shrugged. "We know that there are those among us who do not have a clear picture of communism, but they will have to learn or we will expel them from the Party."

How big a dreamer Mr. Prikryl was became clear very soon. He promised that those who did not care about the problems of the workers would be expelled, and instead, he himself was purged from the Party soon afterwards.

He was replaced as soon as the Secretariat of the Communist Party realized that Mr. Prikryl was not looking at the political affiliation or religious belief or personal grudges of

---

4 Workers are "allowed" to donate to different causes that are espoused by the communists. At one time it might be to further their aims in Korea or the Congo or wherever the communists bosses decided their "charity" should go. Workers are heavily pressured into giving to these causes.

the people he was talking for. His replacement was a really rough communist who didn't care about people. His only concern was what was useful to the Party and himself.

"O. K., Ruda, let's drop this discussion. We will not convince each other anyway. Back to our problem at hand— what do you think would be the best thing for Peta to do?" asked Father.

"Let him go to our *internat.*"

"But what sense is there to spend two years in our factory's *internat* and not know anything in the end of the training anyway?"

"He will learn something useful, don't worry about that," Mr. Prikryl avowed. "I'm thinking about the main reason I have for wanting him at our *internat.* To be able to go to school, he will need a *cadre card* recommendation and if Peta will be in our *internat,* I could help him a little."

Here again, Mr. Prikryl showed his benevolence. He was a big man, a little stoop shouldered, with large, workers' hands, and a slow deliberate manner of speaking. He usually wore worker's overalls and a blue cap. My father was very fond of him, and I remember his saying many times, "Ruda is a good man. He wouldn't hurt a fly." Everyone thought of him in this way because that's the kind of man he was.

He joined the Communist Party when it was first organized. Who could blame him for wanting a better life for his family? That is what he thought he would be providing for everyone—not just himself. It was a fact that before the communist regime he worked very hard, and still he had nothing to show for his efforts. His family barely existed and sometimes they actually went hungry. He saw that other people did not work as hard as he did, and still they had more than he and his family—in some cases, much more. The owners of his factory had big houses, cars, and the comforts of life. The communist agitators came like the serpent in the garden of Eden, and many people like Mr. Prikryl who were downtrodden, were an easy prey. It sounded so reasonable to them they were told: "Why should you have to work so hard? And what does your employer give you? Alms only, that's all. But look at them. With the money you make for them, they live in luxury, sleeping until noon; spending on one meal what it costs you to feed your family for four months. They take the sweat of your brow and turn it into a vacation in foreign countries wearing jewels and furs . . .

"Be with us; be a soldier for a better future for yourself, your children, and the other workers. There will come a time when we, the working class, will take over and then there will not be the rich or the poor. There will not be a distinction between the head of the factory and the ordinary worker. Then we will work for ourselves and no one will spend our money for us in foreign countries."

Naturally, such talk was very tempting for the ordinary worker. Who could blame him for finally succumbing to this pleasant dream? To sow the seeds of hatred in the human heart is always much easier than to cultivate the flower of love in ourselves and our fellowmen. Almost the whole basis of communism is built on hatred. That's why communism can never be a successful solution to the social problems of today. The use of contemptible means cannot eventually bring us to an honest and honorable end.

But Mr. Prikryl and the other followers did not think that far ahead. He just saw himself being exploited by others. He did not like to think of himself as inferior to anyone; he saw himself as an equal to any man. Who among us is different? Not one. We would all like to be bigger than we are. We would all like to have more than we have. We are always looking higher—to be more; to possess more; seldom do we see the injustice done to our fellow men.

At the end of their conversation, Father and Mr. Prikryl decided that I would go to the *internat* that was under the auspices of the factory in which my father worked, so that after one year Mr. Prikryl could help get a favorable *cadre card* and permission for me to go to high school.

71

"If you will go to our *internat*," Mr. Prikryl promised, "you will not have to pay for staying in the one in Prerov. Comrade Stika is so determined for you to be in an *internat* that he agreed to that settlement."

"Ruda, are you sure that Peta will get a favorable recommendation after one year since there are two years of training in our *internat?*"

"Yes, I'm sure. Last week we decided to change the curriculum of the *internat* and make it a one year course only."

"When am I expected to enter the *internat?*" I asked.

"It would be best if you went right away. Go home now and get the things together that you had in Prerov and this afternoon come to the *internat*," Mr. Prikryl suggested. "I will make arrangements for you."

So I went home, and with Mother's help, we packed everything I needed to take with me. I was ready to leave when Father came home.

"Remember, Peta, that you are going there because they want to break you—your character, your personality, your faith. They want you to become a communist," Father cautioned as I was leaving.

I understood what he was trying to say. It was not necessary to say any more—we understood each other perfectly.

With Mother it was different.

"Be a good boy, Peta. Pray every morning and night; remember that every Sunday you are obliged to go to Mass . . ." Mother gave me the same loving lecture that most mothers give their young as they prepare to leave the nest.

8. UNDER SURVEILLANCE

I was met at the *internat* by five boys from my home town. Two were good friends of mine who showed me to the dormitory I was to share with sixteen other boys.

The *internat* in Zamek was much different from the one in Prerov. Instead of being in a beautiful castle with large surrounding gardens, it was on the second and third floors of a three-story building in the middle of the business district of the county seat. The only view from the three windows in the dormitory was the other drab buildings, and the church tower with a big clock. There was only one thing that both *internats* had in common—they had both been confiscated from the owners by the communists.

After my friends introduced me to the other boys, we went to eat in the restaurant where we always ate supper and Sunday's dinner. On work days, we ate dinner in the factory. At breakfast time, we ate in the *internat*. The food was not bad, but we didn't get enough sometimes.

Immediately after supper, I went to report to the director. On his door were the familiar slogans that I detested so much:

We greet each other: *Cest Praci*
We call each other: Comrade

The director, Comrade Desatnik, was a stocky man of about fifty-five. On his coat was the communist's star with the hammer and sickle—the communist's insignia. He was sitting at his desk as I entered. I was immediately struck by the coldness of his piercing eyes.

"Good evening, sir. I'm Peter Esterka. I've been sent from the factory to become an apprentice."

"Obviously you didn't notice the sign on my door," he said very sternly.

"Yes, sir, I did. But I'm under the impression that it is the greeting for members of the Communist Party." I didn't want tell him outright that I could not bring myself to say these words.

"Honor the work and Comrade are slogans for all who belong to the working class, Comrade. And you are now one of us." His eyes had the most penetrating look I have ever seen. It was as though he wanted to read everything that was on my mind. It took a long time for me to get used to that look. Without changing his expression, he leaned back in his chair and said, "Tell me about yourself, Comrade Esterka."

There was no use trying to be evasive. Comrade Desatnik could find out (if he did not already know from my *cadre card*) all he wanted to know. So I told all about myself. When I finished, I added, "And I would like to tell you that I'm a Catholic and I would like permission to go to Mass every Sunday."

Comrade Desatnik was noticeably taken aback.

"I'm afraid you can't go this Sunday because we are going to the *brigada* in the morning."

"Of course, the *brigada* is voluntary, isn't it?" I asked.

Everyone knew it was voluntary, but everyone also knew that if he did not go, it was put on his *cadre card*. That's why the *brigada* was called *Dobrovolne povinna* (voluntary obligation).

"Yes, it is voluntary. But if you wish to get a good *cadre card* and go to school, you have to be as every member of the collective and not as an individualist."

How many times after that was I to hear that I was an individualist and that I didn't want to cooperate with the collective!

"I don't mind working with the collective, Mr. Desatnik, but on Sundays I must go to Mass because I have to fulfill my duty to God."

74

"The others are also Catholics and they don't care about going to Mass."

"I don't know if they care or not, but I know my obligation to go to Mass. And so I'll go next Sunday," I told him firmly even though I was fully aware that my decision would go on my *cadre card*.

"Why do you wish to be different from the others?"

"I don't want to be different. I just want to do what I think is right. That's all."

"You know that going to church will not help you with your *cadre card*."

"Yes, I know. But I can't do anything against God just to please some people."

"Do you really believe in God?"

"Certainly I do."

"Do you also believe what the priests are telling you?" Comrade Desatnik asked very sarcastically.

"Yes, I do."

"I don't," he said emphatically. "Do you know what I think about priests? I think they are stooges of the capitalists. They teach the people how to obey; how to be humble and how to suffer; how to do everything the bosses tell them. They are helping the capitalists to keep the people satisfied with misery. If these people had any sense, they would rise up in hatred and overthrow their oppressors. But the priests see to it that they wallow in their wretchedness so that the capitalists can stay in power."

"You are wrong, Mr. Desatnik," I said as forcefully as I knew how. "The priests and the Church are not in collusion with the capitalists who oppress the working people. Any one who does an injury to his fellowman is committing a sin against charity and it is a very serious sin. *That* is the true teaching of the Church."

Comrade Desatnik was surprised with my answer. His face became flushed with anger. He made a visible attempt to remain calm, but he couldn't control his voice completely as

75

he said, "All priests are of one bunch." He shook his fist in the air. "Not one of them is good. They just try to mislead and deceive the people."

From his voice and expression I could see that he just hated the priests and everything that had any connection with the Church.

"I have another opinion about the Church and priests," I declared. "They are always very good to me and I like every priest I have ever known."

I could see that my words irritated Comrade Desatnik more than I thought they would. He tried to control his temper, but to no avail. And so he said, "Go now, Comrade. We will talk about such problems later. Now, I don't have any more time."

And we did talk about religion very often during the year I spent in the *internat*. Almost every Sunday evening when the others went to the movies or had some other entertainment, Comrade Desatnik invited me to his office for a talk. Such talks had one real purpose—to indoctrinate me. I was aware of it from the very beginning, and Comrade Desatnik confirmed my opinion later in the year when he said, "I have spent so many hours and evenings with you, and yet, you are worse than you were in the beginning."

I suppose I was "worse" in certain ways. Because I had to answer many different questions Comrade Desatnik asked on such "indoctrination evenings;" I was forced to read and study about the Catholic Church, her teaching, and history. I thought that two could play his game as well as one. If he were trying to convince me, maybe I could try to do the same to him.

I never knew what kind of questions Comrade Desatnik might ask. But it was not too difficult to refute his objections, because they were mostly from communistic pamphlets, and Comrade Desatnik was not an educated man. He was just another "old communist" who believed, as Mr. Prikryl did, in the ultimate victory of communism.

76

His objections against the Catholic Church were not against any doctrine. They were just baseless assertions like:

"The priests and the Pope are promoting war. Before every battle they give a blessing to the guns. I can show you a picture of a priest giving such a blessing."

Then he handed me a picture of soldiers kneeling before a priest as the priest raised his hand in blessing.

"I don't see the priest blessing the guns."

"Are you blind then? What do you think he is doing with his hand?"

"He is simply giving absolution to the soldiers. You are only seeing the guns. You overlook the kneeling soldiers," I was not trying to be sarcastic. It was our custom on those "indoctrination evenings" to talk as equals. But one thing I had to remember: everything I said would be repeated somewhere else. That's why I was very careful about answering his questions, especially when they touched on politics. Then I had to be especially careful of my choice of words.

It is very difficult for anyone who has not lived under tyranny to be able to realize and understand what life can be like when every word and opinion must be carefully weighed. But behind the Iron Curtain, a guarded lip is a way of life. To know you are being watched is taken for granted and does not surprise anyone. As much as any human hates to be spied upon, there is nothing that can be done about it.

So it was at the new *internat,* also.

I knew my *cadre card* was not favorable, so it did not surprise me to know that I was being watched and all my words and actions were relayed back to Comrade Desatnik, but I was naturally curious to know who the informer was.

It did not take very long before I suspected "Dric" Kostra, a classmate.

Less than a week after my arrival at the new *internat,* "Dric" asked me if I had filled out an application for membership in the C. S. M.

"No, I haven't," I avowed.

"Here is a form. Fill it out right away so I can take it with me to the county Secretariat."

"Don't worry about me. I'm not applying for membership," I replied.

"But everyone is supposed to be in the C. S. M."

"Not me," I retorted firmly and I turned around and left.

I suspected, but was not sure until much later, that Comrade Desatnik had sent "Dric" to find out my reaction because "Dric" was not an officer of any kind in the C. S. M., and it was not his place to recruit new members for the organization. His father and mother were both communists, so it was natural for him to be Comrade Desatnik's right hand.

From the start, I sensed a strained relationship between "Dric" and myself. For a long time I thought the tension was a result of what happened the day after I came to the *internat*. That was the day for the district soccer playoff of all the *internat* teams. The opposing team was exceptionally good, and our district standing was such that we had to win. A tie would give the championship to our rivals.

As before any championship game, everyone was tense and apprehensive. All conversation was about the game and everyone was discussing strategy for victory.

When I arrived, one of the first to greet me was Jozka, the captain of our team and a very exceptional player. Jozka was a close friend of mine and we had played on the same winning team in our home town. Jozka had all our home town teammates on the front line of attack, except for one spot. That had been my position. It was the position "Dric" played. Although "Dric" was a good player, in Jozka's judgment, he lacked the speed necessary to fill the right wing position.

When Jozka saw me, he was jubilant. He rushed up to me and briefly explained the situation. "You couldn't have come at a more opportune time. Surely you will fill your old position," he exclaimed. It sounded like a good idea to me and, of course, I agreed because I was always anxious for a good game of soccer.

"Now we have most of our old team-mates together again. Our new men are good; we all know our position, and our capabilities. We will surely win," beamed Jozka as he slapped me on the back good-naturedly.

Just before we left for the play-ground, Jozka came to me dejectedly.

"Peta, I'm sorry, but you can't play with us today. Comrade Desatnik overuled me and said "Dric" must play his position since he has been on the *internat* team all this year. You will be only his substitute."

"That's O.K., Jozka, I understand. It's only fair that "Dric" play his position." Truthfully I was disappointed, but I realized Comrade Desatnik was only being fair.

A tremendous crowd turned out to watch the game. Our team played well and hard, and we cheered them from the sidelines, but as the first half came to a close, true to Jozka's fears, we were trailing 1 to 0.

Jozka realized if we were to win, he had to close that weak link in his line of attack. He marched up to Comrade Desatnik and declared, "Comrade Desatnik, our wings are too slow. If we are to win, we need speed. Let me put Peta in "Dric's" place."

Comrade Desatnik finally relented. "O. K. But I expect to win," he emphasized.

We went into the second half with renewed spirit.

Jozka proved himself to be a real captain. Our line of attack was now as deadly as our line of defense.

About midway through the second half, Pepicek, our center, made an exceptional play and set the ball up for me ahead of their defense. One surge of speed, a kick, and the game was tied, 1-1. The crowd went wild.

With only a few minutes remaining, an opposing player, in a desperate attempt to stop Pepicek from scoring, pushed him with his hands, and drew an eleven yard penalty.

The ball was set up. Pepicek drew back his powerful leg and kicked the ball.

The goalkeeper was powerless to stop the bulletlike ball. That kick gave us another score, and the game was ours!

Everyone was wild with excitement and joy. Only "Dric" couldn't forget that I had taken his place in the game.

But the game was not the only reason for the tension between us, even though for a long time, I thought it was. Then one day one of the girls, Eliska, came to me on the playgrounds, and said cryptically, "Peta, be careful what you talk about. "Dric" is spying on you."

"How do you know?"

"I heard him talking to Comrade Desatnik."

"What did he say?"

"They were talking mostly about you. Please, Peta, don't tell anyone that I told you about it," she begged. "It was the day before yesterday. I didn't feel well so I stayed in during the play period. Just before all of you came in, "Dric" rushed into Comrade Desatnik's office. Either Comrade Desatnik forgot that I was in the study room, or else he didn't know it. Anyway, I heard "Dric" tell him all about what you were talking about and with whom he saw you. He said that you refused to play *gorodky* and that you said it is a stupid game."

"Why did he mention my remark about *gorodky?*" I wondered aloud.

"I was thinking about that, too," Eliska replied. "Maybe because *gorodky* is a Russian game."

"It could be. You know, you are probably right. "Dric" thought I don't like *gorodky* because of the origin of the game. He must be really crazy. I just don't like the game because it is not an interesting game. And that's all. But are you sure it was "Dric"?"

"Certainly, I'm sure. I heard his voice very clearly, and I'm positive it was his voice." The girls' study hall was adjoining Comrade Desatnik's office. There was a transom between the two rooms, so Eliska was able to hear the conversation very clearly. She continued, "Please, Peta, don't tell

80

anyone that I told you," Eliska begged me.

"Don't be afraid. I won't."

I don't know why Eliska took a chance and told me what she heard. I had never paid any attention to her. I thought she was a little foolish because she was always talking about her boyfriend, and making wedding plans. She was a member of the C. S. M. when she came into the *internat*, but she was just a nominal member of the Organization, and stayed that way even in the *internat*.

But at last, I knew for certain how Comrade Desatnik always knew so much about what I did and said. I knew, too, why there was a barrier between "Dric" and myself.

Of course, I never revealed to anyone what Eliska told me.

I was sure "Dric" was the informer of many things about me, but still I often wondered how Comrade Desatnik knew so many things about me—things that happened in the dormitory; during the day at work; or in the class when neither Comrade Desatnik nor "Dric" were anywhere around. Once "Dric" and two girls were sent to a C. S. M. conference for two days. Even with "Dric" gone, Comrade Desatnik still brought up subjects that we boys had talked about. He never directly quoted what I had said, but he always touched on the topics that we had talked about and attempted to refute the remarks I had made.

While "Dric" was gone, someone brought up the mysterious death of Jan Masaryk, a Czech foreign minister, and the son of the first president of Czechoslovakia. During the war, young Masaryk was a member of the Czech government-in-exile in Great Britain. After the war was over, he returned to Prague and became a foreign minister in Benes' government. When the communists came to power in February, 1948, he did not escape as many of the other politicians did. Did he believe the communists would not be able to stay in power as so many people did? Who knows?

But not long after the communists came to power, it was

81

announced by radio and newspapers that Jan Masaryk had committed suicide. His body was found under the window of his apartment—he was dead. The radio and the newspapers said it was evident that he had jumped from the window. Of course, by that time, both the radio and newspapers were already completely controlled by the regime. That's why the people did not believe the story was true. The suicides among those who didn't collaborate with the regime were too frequent to be credible.

One of the leaders of *Lidova strana,* who was very active and popular in Moravia, was captured just after the communists came to power. A few days later, it was announced that he hanged himself in his cell. His body was released to be buried, but no one was allowed to open the casket. The communist police guarded it throughout the night before the funeral. But later it was learned that during the night, the members[5] of the family gave some *slivovica*[5] to the guards, and got them drunk. Several relatives opened the casket. It was evident that the man had been beaten to death. The story of suicide had been concocted to cover up the true reason for death.

Of course, I was very careful not to say anything that could be used against me. It was Stalin's era and one could be arrested just for criticizing Stalin, the Soviet Union, or the regime. It was even a "crime" to talk derogatorily about some member of the regime.

So when someone started to talk about Jan Masaryk, I kept quiet. My opinion was: don't get into trouble without having a reason. The summary of the conversation in the dormitory was that Masaryk was murdered. No one said that the communists had done it even though it was clearly intimated.

---

5 Czech whisky made from prunes or sometimes from peaches.

Only four of us didn't say one word during the conversation——one was a boy whose father was in jail for his activity against the communists; two were active members of the C. S. M.; and I.

The following Sunday, to my surprise, Comrade Desatnik touched on Masaryk's death.

"So you think Jan Masaryk's death was not suicide," he challenged.

"Who told you that?"

"I just know it. It isn't important who told me."

"If you know everything, you also know that I never said one word about Jan Masaryk's death." I wanted to leave no room for doubt.

"You know, sometimes even the walls have ears."

After that remark, I was pretty sure there must be a microphone installed somewhere in our dormitory. I was determined to find out where it was. I felt sure there must be one because when the communists took over the Bishop's school, they installed microphones in most of the rooms of the building.

When we went to the playground in the afternoon, I intentionally forgot my tennis shoes. I asked Comrade Desatnik for permission to go back to get them.

Mrs. Desatnik unlocked the door for me.

"I'll be back in a minute," I panted as I ran past her.

I had the tennis shoes ready, but I needed a few minutes alone to see if I could find the microphone if there was actually one there. I thoroughly searched the room, and sure enough, behind the loudspeaker was a microphone. I dared not take it down, but at least I knew for certain that it was there.

The loudspeaker was in the corner of the dormitory and was used for announcements, a signal for lights out and a call to awaken in the morning. Comrade Desatnik played one communistic song on it over and over, day after day and I just hated that song.

I knew the microphone was there and the conversations were monitored, so when the boys in the dormitory became careless in discussing things that could get them in trouble, or when they told jokes about the regime, I always tried to warn them with Comrade Desatnik's words, "Boys, remember even the walls have ears."

9. IDEOLOGY

"Jesus Christ was a communist!"

Comrade Desatnik opened one of his "indoctrination sessions" with that fantastic statement.

I was completely shocked at such an absurd lie. I suppose I looked at him with a startled look because he continued with a sneer, "Certainly Jesus was a communist. He was the son of a proletarian. His father was a poor man and a worker. Jesus Himself became a carpenter, and when He preached, He was always in opposition to the rich people and the ruling class. He associated mostly with the poor and working people. And finally, He was crucified by the Roman oppressors. His whole ideology was revolutionary."

"After what you said the other day about the Church and priests, Mr. Desatnik, I didn't know you knew so much about Christ, His teachings, and His life," I said, not even trying to disguise the irony in my voice.

"The Church and priests only abuse Christ and his teaching," he snorted.

"Mr. Desatnik, you don't really believe that even if you say you do. You know as well as I do that Christ was not a communist. He himself proclaimed His kingship even though His kingdom was not of this world. He said, too, that He is God. Being born poor did not make Him either a proletarian or a communist. I, too, am from a workman's family and someday I'll be a worker myself, but I'll never be a communist. If you'll remember, Christ sometimes reproached the rich people not because of their wealth, but because they were unjust in their dealing with others. All of Christ's teachings had one aim—eternal life in heaven. Because of your almighty materialism, you communists can never accept Christ's teachings. Life hereafter is unfathomable to you. You think everything ends with death. That's why you try to build a paradise on this earth."

"But you'll admit that Christ said 'Woe to the rich,' won't you, Peter?"

"I've already told you that He rebuked the rich because of their injustice to their subjects, not because they were rich. You have the example of Job, who was a good and just man as well as a rich man. God protected Job, but He punished the rich man in the parable about Lazarus. Mr. Desatnik, I wish you could understand that wealth is a gift from God. God gave of His bounty for the betterment of man—not for his detriment. God will not send a man to hell for using His own gifts. Only those who abuse His gifts are to be punished."

"Now I know that you are just parroting what the priests taught. 'Be of service to the rich; keep your mouth shut; work, work for nothing and you will get your reward in heaven.' That's exactly what the capitalists want the priests to teach."

"No, that's not what I meant. I am also against the oppression of the poor and working people. My own family belongs to the working class. Why should I want them or myself oppressed? And you know that I'm not with the capitalists. But I do believe, and the priests believe in the same way, I'm sure, that hatred, killing, and revolution are not the solutions to our social problems. If everyone would keep the commandments God gave us, there would not be oppression, starvation, hatred, and the other evils that are among us."

"Peter, [Comrade Desatnik called me by my first name instead of 'Comrade' and I still addressed him as 'Mister' during our discussions. I still found it extremely difficult to use the word 'Comrade' even though it was becoming a habit—distasteful as it was to me—to refer to all communists by that name] you are an idealist. You know that the capitalists will never change their minds unless we change

86

their minds for them. They will just sit on their money bags unless somebody knocks them off."

"I understand your point. But if that happens, somebody else will take their place and their money and the whole story of oppression and hatred and killing will be repeated again. How can you stop hatred and selfishness? Not by replacing one hatred with another or interchanging victim with tyrant. There is only one source of peace and that is in the love of God."

"All right, you can believe in your God, if you insist. You can even go to church and still you can become a member of the C. S. M."

"You must be joking," I replied.

"No, I'm not. Look how many of the boys and girls go to church and they still belong to the C. S. M."

"Yes, I am aware of that. But they are not good members of either the Church *or* the Organization. If anyone is a good member of the Church or the Communist Youth Organization, he is supposed to keep all of its rules and regulations."

"But there is nothing in our rules that forbids you to believe in God."

"Not explicitly, no," I said. "But in rule five, it says that every *good* member of the C. S. M. is eventually expected to become a member of the Communist Party. Communism and religion are just not compatible. The ideology of communism is materialism. Materialists claim that whatever is not tangible matter does not exist. So how can I became a good member of an organization like the C. S. M. or the Communist Party as long as I believe in God, who is a pure spirit? Convince me that God doesn't exist, that the universe and everything in it were not created by an Infinite Power. Prove to me that it just *happened* to be as it is and then I'll join the C. S. M. Not one moment sooner."

"How can you be so gullible as to believe in something that you have never seen? If God actually exists, why doesn't He show Himself so everyone can believe in Him?"

"He does show Himself. All you have to do is open your eyes and see Him everywhere. God shows Himself in even His smallest miracles."

"Bah! Peter, don't tell me that you even believe in miracles. No one can cure in one moment without medicine."

"No one except God, and that's why Jesus' miracles proved He is God."

"You know, of course, that Jesus is just a myth, don't you? The ancient Jews talked so much about their Messiah's coming that they began to write about him as though He actually existed. In time, others took those writings that were so convincing and believed them and taught them to others. They named their idol Jesus Christ, and finally, because the populace was so ignorant and oppressed, they began to believe such rubbish. Jesus' existence was just somebody's fantasy."

Comrade Desatnik took a complete about-face on his stand of Christ's existence. When he needed Christ's existence to make a point in favor of communism, Comrade Desatnik didn't hesitate to admit that Jesus did exist. He no longer needed Him, so, as communists do, he used whatever story he thought would get his message across. This sort of equivocation was known as dialectic. One moment a communist would use one argument to prove a point. Then, without batting an eye, he would change his stand and use a completely opposite argument to prove the same point. Whatever suited his need at that particular time was the reasoning he followed.

This story was widely circulated to illustrate the meaning the people gave to this reasoning:

A Russian priest was asked by a group of peasants to explain just what the word *dialectic* meant.

He said, "Suppose we take two men as an example. One is clean; the other dirty. Which one needs to bathe?"

The peasants answered. "The dirty man."

"No. He is used to being dirty. The clean one should bathe."

88

The peasants accepted the priest's answer because they respected his priesthood and advanced knowledge. Then the priest asked again, "Take the example of two other men. One is clean; the other dirty. Which one should bathe?"

The peasants replied as one voice, "The clean one."

"No, you are wrong. Why should he bathe? He is already clean."

The peasants accepted his answer without comment.

Again the priest gave the same example of the clean man and the dirty man and asked which one should bathe. The peasants tried to anticipate the reasoning of the priest. Seeing they were at a loss for an answer, the priest said, "Why both of them, of course."

The peasants shrugged and, not wanting to be disrespectful said nothing.

Again the priest, said, "There are two men. One is clean and the other dirty. Which one should bathe?"

The peasants, now completely confused, murmured among themselves as the priest explained, "Neither. The dirty man is used to being dirty; it doesn't bother him to stay dirty. The clean man is clean; there's no reason for him to bathe. So neither of them has to bathe."

One of the oldest men spoke up, "Pope [the Russians call priests "Pope" as Americans call them "Father"], why do you want to confuse us? One time you say one thing. The next time you say something else. No matter what we answer, you say just whatever suits you."

"That's right. Now you understand what the communists mean by *dialectic*."

It was useless to pursue the subject of Jesus' existence any further because Comrade Desatnik had his mind closed on the matter and anything more I said would only make him more cantankerous.

"O.K." I said, "if you don't believe in miracles, how do

89

you explain all the miracles that happen even in this day and time?"

"Don't be ridiculous. There are no miracles happening today."

"Oh, yes, there are. Just take Lourdes for an example. Incurably sick people go there to pray to the Blessed Mother to intercede to her Son for them. Many are physically cured; many more get great spiritual help. What is important and what I'm trying to tell you is that such recoveries come instantaneously without any special effort on the part of the patient. One moment the person is sick, and in the twinkling of an eye, he is completely cured. It must be the hand of God."

Comrade Desatnik looked at me very intently and said very slowly and with great irritability. "Do you really believe this hogwash?"

"Yes, I do."

His expression changed from one of vexation to fury. I had never before seen him look so enraged, even though many times our discussions were heated and our conversation loud. He exploded into a rage like a sudden summer electrical storm. His eyes, which were always so cold and piercing, flashed like lightning. His whole body shook with fury. He jumped to his feet, his arms waving in jerky motions as he shook his fist in my face and his tirade continued. Once I fully thought he was going to slap my face. His voice quivered uncontrollably, and he screamed unmentionable profanities.

Mrs. Desatnik came running into the office from their apartment. "What is going on?" she demanded. "What happened?"

I didn't have a chance to reply because Comrade Desatnik was still shouting, "You stupid idiot! *knezouri ti neco nabulikali, osle jeden,* and you believe it." (Very loosely translated, that would mean something like: That is just the braying of asinine priests.)

"Milosi, please control yourself," Mrs. Desatnik begged.

"What on earth happened? What are you so upset about?" She turned first to him and then to me.

What could I say? I just shrugged. I, too, wondered what had made him so angry. What vital nerve had I hit upon? Was he afraid he might believe in God through His miracles or was the devil defending one of his victims? Even to this day, I still wonder . . .

I vividly remember "indoctrination sessions" such as that as being typical, even though that particular session was the most fierce. During my year at the *internat*, there were many sessions that usually lasted several hours. Strange as they were, they were my catechism classes. I knew I had to be ready for whatever questions Comrade Desatnik posed, and so I did a great deal of reading on religious subjects. I had to give much serious thought to very profound questions that he asked, such as, "Why do you believe there is a God?" Without his query, I probably would have never given too much thought to theology. So, without meaning to, Comrade Desatnik caused me to study my religion more thoroughly than I would have had he let me alone.

Comrade Desatnik didn't change his mind or his philosophy because of our discussions. He was an unbeliever as before. But I think it was only because he didn't want to find the truth—not because he could not.

10. HEROES

"The county president of the C.S.M. would like to talk with you this afternoon, Peter. When the others go to the playground, come to my office," Comrade Desatnik told me.

"Aha! It will certainly be about my refusal to join the organization," I inwardly grimaced and was immediately put on guard.

To talk to Comrade Desatnik, whom I knew very well by that time, was one thing, but to have to explain my reasoning to a stranger was quite another. I was sixteen and bashful, as most boys that age are, so I did not welcome my encounter with the county president.

When I walked into the office, a young man was sitting at Comrade Desatnik's desk. He was alone in the room. He wore the blue shirt with the communist youth organization's insignia on it which was the uniform of the C. S. M.

He looked up and we were both surprised to recognize each other.

There was a strained silence.

After a moment, I said, "Hi."

And he, instead of, "*cest praci*", replied, only "Hi." He looked at me unbelievingly. "So you are the Peter Esterka I've heard so much about."

He still looked a little perplexed. The cards were turned the instant we recognized each other. Before, I had been nervous about talking to the county president of the Communist Youth Organization, but I regained my self-confidence the moment I saw who he was. With him it was the other way around. It was he who was embarrassed at our meeting.

It was not our first meeting even though he was not from that vicinity. Each summer "Comrade President" had come to Hradsko to visit his grandparents who lived there. At that time I saw him regularly at Sunday Mass. He was four or five years older than I, but several times I had let him take my place as an altar boy since he loved to serve Mass but naturally was not scheduled to serve in our parish church.

"You probably know why I am here," he began hesitantly.

"Yes, I do."

But we did not discuss my membership in the C. S. M. Instead, we discussed *his*.

"I had to join the C. S. M. if I wanted to at least finish high school," he said defensively. "I didn't get a good *cadre card* and I had to go to work in the factory instead of being able to attend the university. There was only one possibility for me to get permission to continue my studies; I had to work hard in the C. S. M. So I pretended to go along with the organization. Among other things, I led the choir in the factory where I got a job as a clerk, and from there I was appointed to be the county president. I hope to get permission to go to the university next year."

I was surprised at his story. "I could never do such an underhanded thing," I assured myself. Aloud I said, "How can you do something like this? Doesn't your conscience bother you?"

"I just do what I must. Nothing more. I've got to take care of myself."

"And what about when you must write the *cadre* recommendation for someone? What then?"

He didn't answer my question; he wouldn't even look at me directly. Perhaps he sometimes wrote unfavorable things on mine. Who knows?

"And what about your faith and your belief in God? Can you go to church as the president of the county C. S. M.?"

"No, I can't. I had to stop going to church except when I'm in some town far from here. But I'll change when I get permission to go to school again."

"I don't believe it. And even if you will try to come back

93

"I don't know what I'll do then. Maybe by that time, the Americans will come to free us."

It was strange hearing something like that from the one who was supposed to be the foundation of the future communistic society. But he had told the truth. There was probably no other way to go to school than to collaborate—to change not only one's shirt, but also one's convictions.

Many youths did so. Some of them only feigned loyalty, but others became very helpful to the regime. Some even became good communists. There is an old saying: a lie told a hundred times, becomes a truth. Because they didn't care to find out what was the truth and what was a lie, these people accepted the lie and finally began to believe it.

But there were many young men and women who, instead of betraying their convictions, valiantly suffered and in some cases even died. These are the unsung heroes who fought the battle of life. Surely in their own way, they were victorious. It is possible that some friend or even an acquaintance watched their private fight, and seeing their struggle, gained strength to fight their own little wars. And yet these people were no different from any other people anywhere in the world. They all would have rather led peaceful lives in pursuit of their own individual goals and aspirations. It would have been infinitely easier for them to go along with the trend of the times. But their steadfastness in the face of such adversity was the difference between their being a part of the pack or a hero.

One such hero died in my own village. He was a young man of about twenty-four who escaped from Czechoslovakia when the communists came to power. But he believed that communism must be extirpated from his country so he didn't accept a visa for emigration to a free country, but offered his talents and his life to help fight the enslavers of his homeland. He came back as a spy, working for the American C.I.A. Because he knew the customs, the people, and language as only a native could, he was a real asset. One day

94

someone must have recognized him and informed the police because two policemen rushed to the restaurant where he was eating and asked him to show his identification card. He reached into his pocket, but before he got a chance to produce the card, he was shot. The people in the restaurant witnessed the scene of the young man, lying on the floor holding his card in his hand, moaning his dying breath, "Mother, my mother."

Not everyone who was an adversary of the communists paid with a fast death. There are thousands upon thousands of others who are paying today. They are still suffering in concentration camps, working in mines, or even being "free," but without a chance to live a normal life. They are doomed to menial labor even though many of them are doctors, lawyers, priests, and even Bishops.

One striking example of this was Bishop Otcenasek of the Hradec Kralove diocese. The regime had expelled him from office, and after he was released from prison, he was sent to work in a dairy as a common laborer.

Sometime afterwards, a group of tourists from Holland inquired as to his whereabouts and finally traced him to the dairy.

They could hardly believe their eyes when a man in dirty, tattered work clothes introduced himself as Bishop Otcenasek. His hands, which once wore his episcopal ring as a symbol of his bishopric, were worn and calloused. Everything about his whole appearance showed that he was downtrodden, with the exception of his spirit which remained undaunted.

The other workers were amazed to see distinguished foreigners, who were elegantly dressed, kneel in the muck before their co-worker and ask for his blessing. The Bishop had been forbidden to perform even the simplest priestly duty, so there had not been anything about him to set him apart from the other workers. He had shared the same accommodations and work with never a hint of the prestige he had once possessed. The workers knew, of course, that the apostles were

95

once only fishermen and workers, but they had never dreamed that one of the apostles' successors shared their humble lot. For the most part, the apostles had been able to carry out their priestly mission freely, but Bishop Otcenasek was treated as a common criminal.

As a result of the protest of indignation registered to the authorities by the Dutch visitors, Bishop Otcenasek was later permitted to work in a parish and perform the very minimum duties of a priest, but he was not allowed to administer his see.

One of the older altar boys of our parish who also made an extraordinary sacrifice was Slavek Vana.

He was an exceptional student in every subject even though he had only a little time to study because his father depended on him to do a large amount of the work on the family farm. Because he was a child prodigy, the school board made an exception to their stringent rule, and let him skip a grade. He was several years older than I, so he had already finished high school when the communists started their *Cistku* (they expelled those students, who were not favorable to the communist teaching).

Slavek wanted to attend the university but the "crimes" of his father (his father owned his own farm and the communists considered it a "crime" to own private property), and Slavek's belief in God, and his attendance at Mass each Sunday were big enough reasons for preventing him from attending the university. So Slavek worked as a garbage collector for several years. His superior intelligence, wit, and winning personality made some of the influential communists, who stayed around the court house, relent and they permitted him to continue his studies. He graduated with honors and was offered a job as an assistant professor. It was a very good offer for a young man, and Slavek was glad to accept it.

Just as he was ready to start his new job, the *Kadrovy* (the official who is in charge of the *cadre cards*) informed him

96

to the Church, you will be expelled from the university."
that he could not accept the teaching position unless he joined
the Communist Party.

Slavek refused.

Because all the schools needed good teachers and Slavek
had such outstanding abilities as a teacher, he was allowed
to teach in high school.

After two years, he was issued an ultimatum: "Give up
the Church or give up teaching."

Again he refused.

He was given a chance to reconsider, but he would not
budge from his stand. As a result, his talents and education
were sacrificed and wasted. The only job he was allowed
to hold was a helper on a highway crew.

The most tragic case that I, myself, knew of was the
capture and trial of an anti-communist underground group
that consisted of young men from my district who had been
Boy Scout leaders. Immediately after the war, the Boy Scout
organization flourished throughout the whole country but
was quickly squelched after the communists gained control.
That particular group of young leaders secretly stayed together and started a campaign of harassment and intimida-
tion against the communists. A secret agent of the C. I. A.
was sent to the area and the young men cooperated closely
with him. They kept the new political leaders in a constant
state of agitation by scribbling innuendoes and threats in public places, by collecting damaging information against them,
and by pilfering the armory among other things. One of their
most noteworthy acts was sabotaging the stage used for a big
communist rally and causing it to crumble before the eyes
of about five hundred dignitaries. Their efforts became more
embarrassing and menacing as time went on, and they were
finally captured. The agent was hanged and the young men
got prison terms of ten, fifteen, twenty-five, and thirty years.

The communists implicated the pastor of our parish church
because he had heard the confessions of the young men and

had not reported them. His "crime" caused him to be sent to prison where he spent about twelve years. It's a well known fact that the communists do not want martyrs on their hands, and seeing that the old pastor was dying, they released him from prison, but made him work on a highway crew until he died shortly thereafter under mysterious circumstances.

The assistant priest, who had so heroically saved the village at the end of the war by cutting the wires so that the German observer was not able to warn his army of the advancing Russians, was arrested on two occasions. He spent several years in prison at hard work in the uranium mines in Jachymov. Today he is not in prison anymore, yet he is not allowed to work as a priest. He is, instead, a bricklayer's helper. Even though his heroic feat at the end of the war saved the village and the lives of the people including those who later persecuted him, he was considered "undesirable."

11. TRIAL

From time to time different communists talked to me and tried to convince me to join them. Usually they brought along communistic pamphlets for me to read. There was definitely a strong pressure on me to join the organization but not an urgent demand.

Sometime later in the year at the *internat,* I was told to report to the laboratory of the factory engineer, Mr. Zajic. I did not give the order a second thought because I was often sent to his laboratory to help him make tests of the different kind of plywood we produced in our factory. Mr. Zajic was writing a book and he needed an assistant to take notes as he tested the elasticity, firmness, and flexibility of the wood. He had trained me to be his helper, in spite of or maybe it was because of—my difficulties with the communist authorities. He was an expert in his field, but he was not a communist, which accounted for the reason he was removed as president of the factory after the February, 1948 take-over.

When I entered his office, Mr. Zajic had on his coat and seemed strangely nervous. He picked up his hat and cane and said, "Come with me to the company headquarters."

Mr. Zajic did not speak as we walked along, which was characteristic of him. Sometimes we had spent hours in his laboratory together without a word spoken between us except for whatever instructions he had for me.

We reached the garden between the laboratory and the office building. Mr. Zajic paused and looked around. "Be very careful answering the questions, Peter. Whatever you do, don't talk too much," he warned me.

He looked at me very kindly, almost sympathetically. I wondered what he meant, but I replied "I will" without having any idea to what he was referring.

99

Waiting for us at the entrance was one of the instructors who led us to the conference room.

I still had no idea of what was going on when we entered, and I saw all the local big-wigs of the Party seated behind the table. I was not surprised to see a gathering of communists, but the rank of that gathering was more than I had seen together before. There was the president of the company, Comrade Vacek; the *Kadrovy* (the official in charge of writing the recommendations and the *cadre cards*); the chief of the factory militia; the president of the factory's Communist Party; the president of the union; Comrade Desatnik; the instructor and Mr. Zajic (although he was not a communist). Mr. Zajic was shown a chair behind the table, which he took a little reluctantly. Seated in the back of the room in a corner was my father. I was really surprised to see him in such company. Father looked a little drawn and pale and I started to walk in his direction.

"Sit down here," the instructor motioned me to a chair directly in front of the table opposite all the men. It was only then that I realized that it was I was being "put on the carpet."

It finally dawned on me that I was on trial—for what I did not know. I looked around at my judges. Most of them had talked to me privately about my refusal to join the C.S.M., but this was not just an informal conversation or an invitation to join the Party. This was a serious session and I was afraid I was in for real trouble. It seemed much like a trial except that I, the accused, had no lawyer and the jury (expect for the engineer, Mr. Zajic) was completely biased against me.

"Comrade Esterka," intoned the company president, Comrade Vacek, "I called you here before these distinguished Comrades to advise you that you are living in a different society than you think, or perhaps you know, but you refuse to admit it."

He paused, waiting for me to reply, but I kept silent. So he continued, "Times have changed. We are not living in a

100

society of individuals anymore. We must all move forward together, united so that we will form one body. There is no longer a place for an individual. If someone insists on this foolish selfishness, he is out of step with our society and must be destroyed by it."

Again he paused, but still I said nothing, so he went on, "I understand that you are the only apprentice from our *internat* who is a stubborn enemy of the socialistic and communistic idea that we are trying to make a reality. If you wish to become a member of our new socialistic and communistic society, you must change. You must change completely —your thoughts and actions as well. We don't need or want a reactionary among us. If you do not destroy your reactionary thoughts yourself, then we will have to destroy you. There is no place in our newborn socialistic society for one who hates the working people and their leaders."

Then Comrade Vacek droned on and on about how the old communists had died for a better future for themselves and their children and that we must be grateful for what we have etc. etc. . . .

He, like almost every other communist, was a master in tautology. I had heard these things a hundred times, so I sat silently without interrupting him. I tried to keep the promise I gave to Mr. Zajic. But it was not easy to keep my peace. Only the engineer's cautioning look stopped me several times from saying what I thought about the "people's government."

When Comrade Vacek finished his speech, which in essence was only about how grateful we must be that we lived in the society where there were no slaves or bosses, where we did not have to worry about work, and where the people governed themselves—he asked me directly, "Why are you so stubborn, Comrade Esterka, and why don't you want to cooperate in building a nice future?"

I still made no comment.

"Answer my question, Comrade Esterka," he insisted, looking at me with the very hollow eyes of a man who had

101

not slept for several nights. Even though he was in his early fifties, Comrade Vacek looked much older. His very elegant suit, which he could afford to buy because he was the president of the company, didn't make him any younger or more handsome. He always looked very unhappy. Seeing him looking so tired, it seemed to me as if he had some sickness. Maybe he was sick—not physically but in his conscience. By this time, Comrade Vacek was a very convinced communist. It had not always been so with him. During the Nazi occupation, he was only a very minor clerk in the factory which he later headed. Then, as an insignificant clerk, Comrade Vacek collaborated with the Nazis. His collaboration was not big. Just to say "Heil! Hitler" and to be loyal to the enemy was perhaps not a very big crime, but when the war was over, the Czech people looked on even such small collaboration as a betrayal. So his friendship with the Nazis misled Comrade Vacek to join the Communist Party when the war was over. The communists had enough influence to protect him, and so he was not arrested. He was grateful for it. He *had* to be. So he served. He just served without asking why he was told to do this or that. Because he became a very obedient servant, he became more and more important. After February 1948, his influence grew even faster. First he was the president of the factory where he had worked for many years; later he was the president of the whole company.

As Comrade Vacek's career grew, the more tyrannical he became and the more the employees hated him. But he evidently didn't care what the people thought about him. He had power, lots of money, and he was his own boss as well as the boss of the men with whom he had once worked side by side.

"Answer me! Why don't you want to join the C. S. M.? Why do you want to be different from the other youngsters? Something better, something exceptional?"

"No, sir, that's not true. I don't want to be different from the others," I commented for the first time.

"So what is keeping you from being one of them?"

"I don't think I'm not one of them."

"Yes, you are. All of them are members of the C. S. M., except you, of course. We could have a hundred per cent membership in our *internat* if you would not be there," he said caustically.

"I'm sorry you can't have a hundred per cent membership."

"Sorry, sorry. Don't be sorry. Just apply for membership."

"I can't do it. I just can't do it."

"Tell me why. You must have some reason. Tell me what it is."

"My belief in God," I said with great deliberation.

When I said that, Comrade Vacek sat very quietly in his chair looking at me with a fixed gaze. From the corner of my eye, I saw the engineer. He was looking down at the table as though he were not paying attention to what was going on. Comrade Desatnik did not look at me either. His eyes were glued on his superior.

Slowly Comrade Vacek said, "Comrade Esterka, why are you so bull-headed? Haven't we told you often enough that there is no God? How can anyone who claims to be intelligent say: 'There is a God—but you can't see Him; there is a soul —but you can't see it either?' That's foolishness! Believe only what is real. Doctors have performed operations on every part of the body and still not one of them has ever found a soul."

"Have they ever found an intellect or a will?"

"Don't be impertinent, Comrade Esterka. Certainly not."

"But yet you don't argue the existence of man's intellect or will. You know that we all have thoughts. Yet no one has seen a thought. Doesn't that prove to you that there are some intrinsic things that are intangible and invisible?"

"Absolutely not! Our scientists are making new discoveries all the time. Some day soon they will be able to explain very clearly how a person thinks. Then we will have mastery over the human mind. Just recently the great Russian biologist,

Olga Lepeshinskaja, has discovered a way to produce life artificially."

At that time, Olga Lepeshinskaja was a Russian biologist who had won the Stalin Prize and the dictator's favor by dedicating her "scientific" work to Stalin. Immediately after her work was made public, biologists the world over found that she was in error, but she remained the biological heroine of the U. S. S. R. until Nikita Khrushchev himself repudiated her work after Stalin was denounced. Now even Russia disclaims her work, but at the time I was in the *internat,* no one dared to criticize her.

"I still believe that there cannot be life without God as the motivating force," I asserted.

Comrade Vacek's face grew less intent and he leaned back in his chair and laughed, "How very backward you are, Comrade Esterka. Why, years ago when I was in high school, we proved that we could produce life. We put plain, clear water in a glass. Then we put some grass that was obviously dead into the water and set it in the sunshine. The next day we found very minute living beings when we put the grass under a microscope."

"And what did *that* prove?" I asked, trying to act very blasé.

Comrade *Kadrovy* tried to interrupt the conversation and change the subject, but Comrade Vacek went on, "It proves that you can get living creatures from unliving matter if the conditions are favorable. Therefore, you see, we don't need God for creating living creatures."

He laughed in a kind of condescending tone that I could no longer tolerate.

My parents had always taught me to be respectful to my elders, but I felt that in this case, it was not a question of courtesy or age. It was a question of basic principles—to me the most basic principle of all—the existence of God. God had to be the foundation of every moral aspect of man's existence; the history and tradition of every nation, or every

104

thought and deed of each man would have a different value. That is why I didn't see that Comrade Vecek was an old man to be respected. He was an opponent who was attacking the core of all life. Even Mr. Zajic's warning glance did not stop me.

"I am surprised," I mimicked, "that you, a man who claims to be modern and progressive, could not only use, but also believe such an argument. You claim that I am backward and that I hold obsolete views when I say that I believe in God. Don't feel sorry for me. It would be better if you examined your own theory because it is the opinion of what you called the Dark Ages. Today everyone knows that worms are not hatched from meat or that flies do not breed from squalor. As far back as the nineteenth century, Louis Pasteur, the Frenchman, proved without a doubt that spontaneous generation of living organisms does not take place. In the Bishop's school, under the direction of the Jesuits, whom you communists accuse of being the most uneducated and unscientific teachers of all, we did the same experiment you spoke of, except that our experiment was done to prove that there is life even in plain water and in the air. Who then teaches from the darker ages—the Jesuits or you? Is what you are talking about really science or is it quackery to serve your purpose? If the people of old days believed that the world was flat and not round, or the wise men of Galileo's day did not appreciate his findings, it was because they did not have a chance to understand these things before that time. But if someone today still believes in spontaneous generation and uses it as an argument to prove that God does not exist, then all I can say is that any really modern progressive man can feel nothing but sympathy for such ignorance."

My insult was like setting a hot iron to Comrade Vacek's pride. He jumped to his feet, pounded the table with his hand and yelled at me incoherently, "Now I know where you belong. The concentration camp is the right place for you and not the high school . . . I'll destroy you . . . Completely . . .

I'll show you what we do with mules like you . . . You'll be thankful to get work in the mines . . . You'll go to school all right, but it will be a hundred meters under the ground . . . You'll come back and beg for a pardon . . . But I'll not give it to you . . . You must be *destroyed!* And don't think that the American capitalistic gangsters will come to rescue you . . . We'll reign forever . . . Here, now, and later in America, Germany, and everywhere. . . . We communists will destroy them all, as we will destroy you and all who are against us."

Comrade Vacek was furious. After what seemed like an interminable time of raving, he stormed into his adjoining office and slammed the door.

During his absence, no one moved from his place. Only the members of the commission spoke a little among themselves, and they only whispered.

I turned to look at my father. He looked so forlorn, so I rose to go to talk with him just as Comrade Vacek appeared in the door again. Everyone kept silent. I was well aware that I had pushed him as far as I dared, and I sat down.

"Comrade Esterka, it is evident to me now that your place is not in high school; it is not even in our *internat,* but in a concentration camp where they really know how to change your convictions. But since I am a very good-natured man, I want to help you. I'll make a compromise with you. I'll forget everything that I found against you, if you will join the C. S. M. I'll do even more—much more. I know you are a good boy, smart, too. Your biggest stupidity is your stubborn belief in God. I know you don't deserve it, but I'll give you one big chance. If you will join the C. S. M., I assure you that you will be appointed president of the county organization in two weeks. You'll get permission to go to high school immediately. Then you can go to the university. We'll give you a very nice scholarship. You will not have to depend on the support of your parents; you need not have any qualms about them. I promise you also that during your vacation from school you can go to foreign countries and even spend some time at the coast. What about it?"

Comrade president waited for my answer.

The things he offered were all the things I could only have dreamed of. To go to high school and to get a scholarship to the university was the most I ever dared to hope for. But to travel and even spend a vacation at the sea-side was fantastic. I'd probably be sent to Russia, Bulgaria, Poland, Rumania, or maybe even East Germany, when I could escape into the American zone of Berlin without risking my life (at that time there was no wall in Berlin). Just the possibility of foreign travel and a chance to escape might be worth joining the C. S. M. for a few years.

But my thoughts were shattered when I realized the price Comrade Vacek bargained with me was a little higher than the thirty pieces of silver Judas took for betraying Christ. But it was not high enough to buy my convictions and my faith which I did not cultivate in only one year. It was slowly built first by my parents, then by my teachers and the priests who taught me in school. There was also my part in the cultivation of my faith, the long conflicts with my own nature and temper, and with the devil himself; the lone struggles to do what was right when it was so very difficult at times.

No, I couldn't betray all those who believed in me. And I couldn't betray myself. Most of all, I couldn't betray God. Nothing on earth was worth that price.

"I can't do it," was my answer.

"Don't give an answer just now. Think about it a little. I'll give you time. You can come to me any time if you'll accept my offer. You have until the beginning of the new school year to make up your mind."

"My answer is 'No,' and I'll not change it," I insisted.

Comrade Vacek was dumbfounded. "Don't be stupid. Take my offer," he coaxed. "If you don't, you know what you can expect. Remember that we have concentration camps even for youths!"

The "trial" was over. It was 5:30 p.m. We had been in

the conference room three and a half hours. Father and I walked out into the lengthening shadows of the waning day without saying a word. Each of us was absorbed in his own thoughts. I had been released by the commission but the devil was trying desperately to take hold. I could walk and move around at will, but the devil stayed close, still trying to make me succumb to Comrade Vacek's offer.

Imagine! High school, a scholarship, the university, travel and worldly success! All this could be mine. To yield would have made everything so simple. To resist was so terribly hard.

I sensed that Father, too, was being tormented. It must have been insufferable for him to ask a son to hold fast to principles that were being discarded on every side and to face instead a life of suffering in a concentration camp.

When we reached the station where Father was to catch the bus to go home and I was to go in the opposite direction to the *internat*. Father said slowly and sadly, "Maybe you could take the offer."

"Do you really mean it?" I asked in amazement.

Father didn't answer. His eyes fell to the ground.

"To betray you and everything you've taught me? No, Father. Never!"

He took my hand in his and gripped it tightly and whispered hoarsely, "Thank you, Peta. I knew I could trust you."

I noticed tears in his eyes as he turned to leave.

We understood each other.

12. WORKERS' PARADISE

My *internat* training was completed. Except for our ideo-
logical differences, I had made sure that none of my superiors
had any reason to be displeased with me because I knew that
their personal regard for me was the only thing between me
and the concentration camp. I was afraid that one bad report
that called unfavorable attention to me would surely have
prompted Comrade Vacek to fulfill his threat.

At the end of the year, we took an oral examination before an examining commission that consisted of a delegate
from the county Secretariat, the *Kadrovy* from the factory,
and Comrade Desatnik. Comrade *Kadrovy* had taught us political science, and in the examination he asked me to explain
the evolution of society from the dawn of civilization, beginning with the formation of tribes down though the "per-
fection" of communism.

I had heard the communists' version of that question a
hundred times so there was little chance that I could have
forgotten. I dutifully answered what Comrade *Kadrovy* had
taught us: "As there is a basic law in physics that for every
force there is a counter-force, so it has been in the evolution
of society."

I briefly explained Marx's theory which claimed that everything from the lowliest plant life to human society has been
constantly changing and struggling since the beginning of
time. From this change and struggle comes progress and a
better society. He claimed that in every human society there
is the dominant power (a thesis) that holds the means of production and wealth. An opposing class (an antithesis) arises
and seeks to overthrow the dominant power. After a struggle,

109

a brand new class (the synthesis) emerges that takes on the best of both of the old classes, and in turn, becomes a new dominant power (a new thesis). After a time, a new opposing class forms and the process of change and struggle begins again. Marx maintained that this struggle always produces a higher degree of civilization, but he did not explain why some of the bad elements of the two forces did not seep in along with the good.

Briefly Marx's theory of the evolution of society is this: first came slavery. A struggle ensued and from this strife, feudalism developed. Feudalism then became the dominant power, but because of its imperfections, a new antithesis formed. This struggle continued over several centuries and finally capitalism emerged. Marx claimed that the flaws in capitalism would breed a new opposing force, the proletariat, who would arise and overthrow capitalism, leaving socialism as the power. Socialism would eventually give way to communism. But since communism would be, in Marx's estimation, a perfect society, there would be no more counter forces to seek to destroy it.

As I had been taught, I ended my answer with: "Until communism there was a conflict between the ruling class and their subjects. But under pure communism, there will no longer be a counter-force because there will be no oppressing force. According to Marx-Leninism, society will be at the summit of evolution under pure communism. There will not be any more changes because everyone will be equal, happy, and completely satisfied. There will no longer be the oppressed or the oppressors. There will be a paradise on earth."

Certainly it was a tongue-in-cheek answer that I could never believe, but it was the only answer I could give and still hope to pass.

After the exams were finished, I returned to the class-room to get my grade. Comrade Desatnik seemed very pleased with my work.

"You answered Comrade *Kadrovy's* question very well,

Peter Esterka was twenty-one years old at the time of his escape from Czechoslovakia. Up to this time he was refused permission for higher education because of the religious tendency of his family and his own "subversive and nonconformist" ideas.

The long stretch of "no-man's land" near the Iron Curtain was guarded by a high watchtower and gun nest. Beyond a mine-infested field, three series of wires, some of them electrically charged had to be crossed in order to get to the border and freedom. The consequence of being caught in an attempted escape was certain imprisonment.

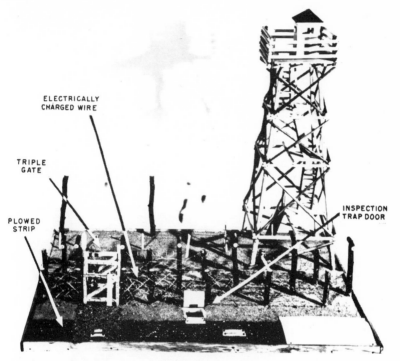

ELECTRICALLY
CHARGED WIRE

TRIPLE
GATE

PLOWED
STRIP

INSPECTION
TRAP DOOR

Model of a sector of the Iron Curtain on the Bavarian-Czechoslovak border. It was constructed in 1955; since then additional security facilities have been added.

On March 9, 1963, Peter Esterka was ordained in
Rome. He celebrated his first Mass on the following
day.

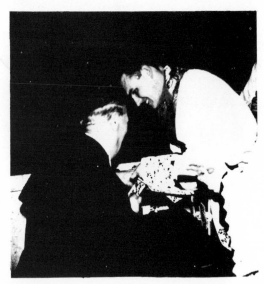

Father Esterka with Cardinal Ottaviani, who attended the Mass and reception, giving his con-
gratulations.

Josef Cardinal Beran, Archbishop of Prague, is shown with Father
Esterka during a visit to Shiner, Texas. Cardinal Beran had been exiled
to Rome.

Peter relaxes a bit in Vienna on the way to the refugee camp where they would have to spend some months; however, there are now alternatives from which to choose a future.

The day after their escape, Peter and Jara pose with their interpreter in Vienna while Pepek takes their picture; their sole possessions: their lives, their clothes and the few packages Peter is holding.

Pepek, Jara, Father Skalicky, who is a secretary to Cardinal Beran, and Peter pose during a visit in Rome. Jara is now married and works for the Navy in the United States.

Peter. But what I am interested in is: what is your own private opinion to the question?"

I hesitated to tell him because I was afraid he would change my grade so I tried to evade the question.

"Don't be coy. I know you pretty well by now, and I doubt that what you answered was your own opinion. Don't worry, your grade won't be changed. I am just curious to hear what you really think."

"I'd rather not, Mr. Desatnik, but if you insist, I'll tell you," I ventured. "I don't believe there can ever be complete equality in any society. No two people were ever made identical. Just look at your finger tips. Of all the billions of people who have ever lived, only *you* have those same finger prints. They are a sign to you that God made you a little different from every other human being. We were never meant to be carbon copies of each other, and no amount of education or progress will make us so. As far as a paradise on earth, we had one once and lost it. The only paradise we can hope for will come to us after death. There will never be another here on earth."

"Peter, you are as stubborn today as you were the day you came. I had hoped that during your stay here I could convince you that communism will bring a real paradise to the workers. It's too bad that you can't see it."

It was true. I could not see the paradise they claimed to be building.

After three weeks vacation at home, those of us who finished the course at the *internat* were sent to factories all over the country. One boy called Jenda (who was my best friend in the *internat*), three girls, and I were sent to the factory where we had been trained and where my father also worked.

During our *internat* training, we had trained briefly in each department of the factory. We were drilled in each step of the manufacture of plywood and wood veneers. But the last several months of *internat* training were devoted to specialized training in the department to which we were to be assigned at the end of the course. We became proficient at every ma-

111

chine and learned in detail each operation of that department.

On the first day at the factory I was assigned to the department I had been especially trained for. But I didn't need any training to perform the job I was given. I swept the floor, carried away the rubbish, and did whatever menial work there was to be done. I worked in that department only one day. After that I worked at the most degrading jobs in the factory. My friends who came with me to the factory were given very good jobs in the department for which each of them was trained.

I was thoroughly discouraged because I knew my qualifications were good, and I was sure that my abilities warranted more than the job of janitor. I realized that Comrade Vacek and the other communists were behind my ostracism. It was another of their ways to remind me again: "No matter how smart you are, Comrade Esterka, you just can't break through the wall with your head. Under the auspices of the Party, you you could swim the whole ocean even though now you are only a little fish. But you insist on trying to swim against the tide, and so you will get nowhere."

But there was one way I was able to prove to myself and to them that I could excel without their help. I was still active in sports, especially in track. At that time, I held the 60 meter dash title in our town, county, and district, and earned the right to go to *Mistrovstvi Republiky* (national championship). Ordinarily an athlete who was in the committee's favor was given an easy job working only a few hours a day in the factory, and then he was free to spend as much time as he wanted in training. Because I was not allowed such preferential treatment, I wanted all the more to prove that whatever success I achieved would be on my own.

To participate in the 60 meter dash at the national level, an athlete had to have a district record of 7.3 seconds or less.

In the national races, the contestants were put in groups of fives. From each heat, the first and second place winners of every group advanced to be regrouped for the next heat. This process continued until the finals. In the first heat, I placed first; I came in second in the next race; and I placed fourth in the final heat.

After the race, an official of the district office of sports offered me a good job with the possibility of going to high school. To get the job, I would have to continue training and join their track team, which sounded very good to me. I was enthusiastic until I learned that membership in the C. S. M. was a prerequisite for the job. So the hope of education through sports was also gone.

All I could hope for was my job in the factory.

The work there was not complicated or difficult. I certainly didn't need to be trained to sweep and pick up rubbish, and yet each evening I went home exhausted, not physically, really, but whatever fortitude I may have had was slowly being drained away.

Once again I was tormented with questions to which I could not find the answers. "Why did I bother to try to be good in the *internat?* I did not really want to go there in the first place, so why did I waste a year and get nothing for it? If there is no place for me in this society anyway, why do I even try?"

I groped, but I could not find an answer. I felt terribly dejected.

It was evident by then that the Americans were not coming as we had prayed. More than the year of which Uncle Jirka spoke had gone. The political situation had deteriorated almost beyond salvation. Living conditions, too, worsened sharply. Communism had permeated every facet of life. The Iron Curtain had descended and strangled my country like a hangman's noose. Our subjugation by the communists was not a threat—*It was a stark reality!*

Many times before I had thought of escaping from Czechoslovakia. When factory life become most dismal, the idea kept coming back like a haunting tune. More and more I began to think of the possibility of escaping. I realized that leaving was my only hope of ever being the kind of man I wanted to be. So from then on, I began to give very serious thought to escaping. I started to pay close attention to everything I heard or read that had any connection with the border or the Iron Curtain.

My first paycheck was added fuel to my misery. It was so very small. The department I was trained for was supposed to be one of the best paid in the factory and yet, my friend Jenda, was paid three times more, and even the girls, who worked in a much lower paid department than I, got twice as much.

I felt my problems and convictions were my own business, so I hadn't said anything to my parents about my difficulties at the factory because I did not want to worry them. Besides, I wanted to be self-reliant. But when my first wages came and I took it home to them, I knew they were terribly disappointed, too, because they were in dire need of an extra salary. They understood why my pay was so small and they didn't say a word about how meager it was. I had wanted to be able to help alleviate their distress, but I could not even do that very well.

Before the communists came to power, our financial condition was fair. After they took over, our circumstances grew continually worse, so that by the time I went to work, our situation at home was desperate. None of my family ever had so much to eat that we could say we had eaten enough. And it had been several years since we had bought any new clothes. My father's rule was: "First of all, we have to eat, only then can we buy other things." So we did without.

At that time, eight years after the war, we still had rationing. Each family was given a card that supposedly permitted it to buy essentials. Everyone was to be treated alike. Yet, when it came to actual practice, those who were sympathetic to the communist cause, were able to buy more and

114

get it at a much reduced price because they were issued special cards.

Everyone bought the same products at the same stores, but there were two price standards. For example, a preferred buyer could buy one kilo of sugar for 11 korun at the state owned co-op. But someone like my family had to pay 140 korun on the *volny trh* (free market) for the same kind of sugar because we couldn't get the cards. It was the same with other staples. The prices we had to pay were astronomical compared with those on the standard market, and often we did not have enough money to buy even the necessities. Like most American women, my mother counted calories, but unlike American women, she counted them to be sure her family was getting enough to survive.

My father's hair was quickly turning gray, and my mother also began to show her age. They were truly being put to the acid test. It was one thing for my parents to have high ideals when only they were concerned, but when they saw their growing family in need, it must have taken supreme courage for them to sustain their beliefs. And they were not alone by any means; there were, and still are in my country, many thousands of noble people like my beloved parents who still carry this tremendous cross.

Another bitter pill that was so hard for the people to swallow was the state's collection of products the people raised. Everyone who raised hogs, or any other products, were obliged to "sell" part of them to the state when they butchered. The amount the state demanded depended on how large the family was and how many hogs, or how much land the family owned. Sometime the state's part was half the hog. The owner received a ridiculously low price from the state, but there was no alternative. Whenever his own family needed additional lard, the owner would have to buy back the very products he had raised and was forced to sell. Of course, when he bought them back, he had to pay the higher price of the

115

Volny trh (free market) for his own products.

Once I saw a man who was fulfilling his "duty" by taking five kilos (about 10 pounds) of lard to the state co-op. As he passed, he held up the container of lard and said begrudgingly, "Look, I'm putting this on the working man's table. They will pay me 40 korun for one kilo, so I'll get 200 korun. But because I need it to feed my kids, I'll have to buy it right back and they will charge me 80 korun for each pound. So I'll have to pay them 400 korun for the same package. I'm carrying. That's socialism!"

After a few minutes, we saw him going home with the very same container of lard. "I just stole 200 korun from my family," he complained. It had cost him 400 korun to buy back the lard that he had produced and needed for his family.

My mother still owned a small piece of land, and was able to raise a few potatoes, vegetables, and wheat to help us through the worst years. Occasionally we were able to buy a little milk or butter directly from some farmer, which helped both the farmer and us. The farmer got a much fairer price for his products, and we did not have to pay the exorbitant price of the *Volny trh* (free market).

Not everyone was in the same financial straits as we. Some people had it better, but there were others who were even worse off. We, at least, always had something to eat.

Sometime around Christmas, I was appointed to the clerk's job in my department. It was not because Comrade Vacek had suddenly become generous. He had not. The truth was that I was lost in the throng of workers in the factory and no longer had the "bad influence" I had had on the other young people in the *internat*. Since I was no longer a thorn in his side, Comrade Vacek didn't bother to send me to the concentration camp as he had threatened.

My new job consisted of keeping books and making out the payroll in my department. I previously had some training for the job, so when the regular accountant became ill and could not work any more, I replaced him simply because they had no one else trained.

I assumed that with a higher classified job, my salary would be increased, but that was strictly my assumption. My pay remained the same. My friend, Jenda, was already planning to buy a motorcycle—the dream of every teenage boy—while I still did not have enough money saved to buy an overcoat which I needed so badly.

My next job was certainly more to my liking than the job of janitor. Working in the office gave me a vantage point to observe the workings of the socialistic economy in practice. I saw socialism as it really is—not just in graphs and charts, but I was able to see positively who was taking home the larger salaries, and who was getting favorite treatment. As a sort of hobby, I began to observe the workers themselves. Then I realized that Uncle Jirka was right when he said the factory would be a classroom in the school of life.

Theoretically, only the workers who worked most diligently in furthering socialism were eligible to get special treatment. But one woman in my department was conspicuous for the awards she got in spite of how little work she actually performed. Some of the awards came directly from the President of Czechoslovakia. Comrade Kupilova not only had the easiest job in the department, but perhaps the easiest in the whole factory. Her job was only to feed wood into a machine while her partner and coworker had to sort, grade, and pick up her scrap wood after it came out of the machine. Her partner worked much harder than Comrade Kupilova, but his pay was much less and he never got any awards.

The awards Comrade Kupilova received didn't consist in honors only. There was extra money and a special book called *Udernicka knizka* that went with them. The owner of the book was entitled to buy different things that no one else could get such things as: tropical fruit, radios, or material for building a house.

117

Comrade Kupilova was not held responsible for anything either. Whenever something went wrong, she blamed the director of the department, and he was scared to death to say anything against her. With a temperament like hers, everyone made sure he did not cross her.

It was common knowledge that the reason Comrade Kupilova had such special treatment was that she had real power as a high member of the Communist Party. She even had all the officers of the county Secretariat eating out of her hands. Maybe they too were afraid to say anything against her.

Just the opposite from Comrade Kupilova was a man named Karel Krejcirik. There were all sorts of conjectures about him. From the time I first came to the factory, it seemed to me that there was a bit of mysery about him. Even the nickname of "Yankee" had an unusual ring. I greeted him each morning, and he always returned my greeting but said nothing more, so I often wondered about him and often watched him at work.

I saw that "Yankee" was one of the hardest workers in the department, and yet his salary was one of the lowest.

When I asked the foreman why "Yankee's" pay was so low, he explained, " 'Yankee' came to this factory several years ago as a middle aged man. He was appointed to the machine at which you now see him. But he had the misfortune of replacing a young man who had earned a *udernicka knizka* for bringing up the efficiency of the machine from four to twelve blocks of unfinished plywood in a single shift. The young man was promoted but the norm for the machine had been set and poor 'Yankee' cannot possibly keep up the pace of the man before him. So his pay stays low. And yet, you know, I've never heard him complain. In fact," the foreman continued, "to tell the truth, I haven't heard him say much of anything. He keeps pretty much to himself."

So I wondered all the more about him.

One day "Yankee" came to my office. I was surprised he

118

took time out to talk to me since we had exchanged only greetings before.

"I heard you would like to go to high school," he said.

"Yes, that true, but I doubt that I ever will."

"How old are you?" he sounded genuinely interested.

"Eighteen," I replied.

"You haven't lost anything yet. You will have plenty of time," he remarked in a tone that seemed to convey his encouragement.

"I'm not so sure about that," I confided. "It's been over two years that I am here and there are no prospects that the situation will ever change."

"They cannot keep people in slavery like this forever. Sooner or later the people must do something about it."

Everyone who has ever lived as we did would understand what he meant.

We talked on a little while and somehow the conversation turned to him.

"I am curious about your name. How did you happen to get a name like 'Yankee'?" I inquired.

The story he told me was much more interesting than all the conjectures I had heard about him.

"I was originally from a small town near here. When I was twenty, I left Czechoslovakia and went to America. That's why they call me 'Yankee.' I was young and willing to work like you, so I soon found a good job in a glass factory. I saved my money and was soon able to send for my girl friend. She came and we married. We were happy with our new life and we made many friends. Everything was going very well except that we never had any children.

"We wrote home often and kept in touch with our families until the war. Then we lost contact with all our relatives. When the war was over, my brother was able to write to me again and say that my father had died during the war. It was a terrible blow to me because I had always loved my parents very much. My brother related how hard life had been for

119

them during those years during and immediately after the war. But soon his letters had a different tone about them. He seemed excited over the changes that were going on in Czechoslovakia. He said life was becoming a paradise on earth and urged me to return.

"Oh, he painted a pretty picture all right. He said when a worker got sick, he could go to the hospital or even a sanatorium and never have to worry about paying the bill. He claimed that there was plenty of work for everyone and the salaries were excellent. Even fine vacations were free. He wrote that the workers owned the factories and no longer slaved for someone else. He said it was such a good feeling to know that the factory was your own property and that you worked only for yourself. He even promised that I would get a big new house if I would return.

"Such letters kept coming regularly. I didn't recognize them as communistic propaganda. I had no reason to doubt my own brother. He kept begging me to come back and help the Czech people build a new life."

"Is that the reason you came back?"

"No, I wrote my brother and told him that my wife and I were satisfied with our new life. I had a good job and was a foreman of a small department in the glass factory. We were settled there and my wife and I wanted to stay in America. It wasn't until he wrote that Mother was sick and wanted to see me again that made me unsure of our decision. Then Mother herself wrote and begged me to come so that she could see me once more before she died. I didn't know what to do. I loved her very much and wanted to grant her last request, so we decided to come back. We believed what my brother had written, but actually, it was for Mother's sake that we came back.

"It didn't take long before we realized it was a big mistake. We saw that the situation was not at all as my brother had written."

120

"Does your brother really believe everything he wrote you?" I asked.

"I think he believed it then, but he doesn't anymore."

"What opened his eyes?"

"I told him about my life in America and he sees how I'm living now. Instead of a new house as he promised, I live in two rooms in a dilapidated old shack with no running water except when it rains. Then we literally have to use umbrellas inside our apartment because the roof leaks like a sieve.

"My brother can also see what kind of salary I get and how hard I have to work. He can't visualize how nice we really had it in America. He is in better circumstances than I because he belongs to the Communist Party, but even he realizes that things are not the way he said they were. He was being deceived when he wrote to me. He admits now that he has never seen those things in practice. It was just what he was told would happen as soon as the workers won their struggle. He realizes now that if one gets sick, he really has to be bad off before he can go to a doctor, and then to get his approval to go to a hospital is next to impossible. Even my brother has not had the wonderful vacations he wrote about. Oh, sure, there are some that do. But one sees who they are. And if all that were not bad enough, the taxes are so staggering that we cannot do anything to better ourselves. So what can we do?"

"It must be very hard for you to reconcile yourself to this life. Aren't you angry with your brother for bringing you here?"

"I was at first. But then I realized that *he* did not bring me back. I came of my own free will. I came to see my mother. I know now that it was a mistake not to go back before my visa expired. But just at that time, Mother was dying and I didn't care what happened to me. I lived only to make her last days more comfortable. Then she died, and by the time I came back to reality, it was too late. We had

121

already signed the papers saying we wanted to stay here. We didn't realize what we were doing. But what is done is done."

"Couldn't you get a better job? You said you worked in the glass factory. We have the *Karlovarske sklo* (glass works) here. With your experience, maybe you could get a job there," I suggested.

"There's no use worrying about it. I had a chance for an easier life. They called me to the district court house and wanted me to propagandize against the capitalists and the United States. I had a choice: work for them or spend the rest of my life doing hard work. So I chose hard work because I think it is better to have a clear conscience than a full pocket."

It was heartening to see a man who could take such shabby treatment and still personify charity so beautifully.

Not too long after my conversation with "Yankee," about thirty men in an adjoining department went on strike. In my country, a strike was unthinkable because who were they to strike against? They were told that they worked only for themselves. Only hopeless desperation would drive men to commit such a "crime," but the conditions and pay were so intolerable that the men rose up in rebellion. "We will not work until you give us higher wages," the men hooted.

Comrade President Vacek was called. He came immediately, accompanied by the president of the company union. In free countries the union supports the men and works incessantly to settle their grievances. That is not the case behind the Iron Curtain. There, the Communist Party controls everything, the unions and management alike. There is no such thing as workers' rights or management's prerogatives.

"The workers have the government in their hands" is another communistic slogan that can be seen plastered on factory walls, entrance gates, and almost anywhere else. It is the keynote of workers' rallies and speeches.

But it did not take the strikers long before they saw how

empty their hands were. They not only did not have the reins of government in their hands, they did not even have a right to bargain.

The factory militia moved in and the men were issued an ultimatum to either go back to work or be fired. Within two hours, the strike was squelched and the men were back on their jobs.

Instead of a raise in pay, Comrade Vacek ordered that each man pay a fifty korun penalty for the two hours he did not work.

Obviously there was no paradise on earth for workers!

13. FIRM RESOLUTION

About New Year's 1954, Comrade Vacek was replaced as company president by a very able, younger man who was not a communist, but who knew how to run a factory efficiently. When the communists took control of Czechoslovakia, they put their own people in key positions. But no matter how dedicated to communism a person might have been, he was not necessarily an able manager. Often these people were not qualified for their jobs and, as a consequence, efficiency and productivity usually suffered. In such cases, trained men with no political sympathies were put in charge of factories. About that same time, the communists began to turn their attention to all different types of technology. Realizing there was a lag in the number of potential technicians, they began to encourage factory workers to go back to school. It was the break I had been waiting for.

During the time I had worked in the factory, each new semester I had applied for admittance to high school. Each time I applied, I was turned down. In the light of more emphasis on education, my prospects looked much brighter.

Even though my family needed the little money I brought home, both of my parents insisted that I try to go back to school. They pointed out that since my salary was so extremely small anyway, they would not especially miss getting it. So I jumped at the opportunity to apply again.

I took the prepared application to the new president of the company, Mr. Kozacek, who was noted among the workers for his disinterest in politics. Either he did not look at my *cadre card,* or he ignored it, I don't know, but he signed his approval of my application without asking one question.

I took the application to the principal of the gymnasium

124

(type of high school) in Zamky, the town where the factory and *internat* were located, because there was no gymnasium in our village of Headsko. I commuted the four and a half miles to school by bus each day as I had done when I worked in the factory.

The principal accepted my application and asked me to report on Monday morning for the entrance exam. I had been out of school for a long time and I was "rusty" and needed to do much cramming to prepare for the exam.

It was then Saturday afternoon, so I had the rest of the weekend to study, but I hardly knew where to begin. As I left the school, I thought of Marka's brother (Comrade Stika's former friend). He was always willing to help a young person in any way he could, and best of all, he had been a teacher himself in happier days. He readily agreed to tutor me. We sat up most of that night and all the next day, going over the questions he thought might be asked on the exam.

Monday morning I reported at school for the test. Because it was mid-term, I was the only student entering school at that time. Since I did not have much time to study Russian, I dreaded that test most of all. The Russian language teacher, Comrade Mladenka, was a young woman with a very congenial disposition. I soon found that even though she was a communist, she had a heart of gold and was dedicated to her students.

"I'm afraid I'm pretty poor in Russian," I explained uncertainly.

"Don't worry. You'll pass it all right. I'll help you all I can." And she did. Because of her coaching I was able to pass with no trouble.

I was fortunate to be put into the class of which Comrade Mladenka was home room teacher. She was very patient and went out of her way to help me keep up with the class during the first few crucial weeks.

One of the first things I noticed about school at this time was the many changes that were apparent. Communism was

125

even more deeply imbedded than ever before. School was not just a place where a student could absorb knowledge and develop socially; it was a hot-house for budding communists.

A shrewd student could get by with very little studying if he learned the communistic line very well and knew the bare essentials of each subject. For example, in geography, if one were told to comment on Italy, he could simply say: "Italy is the boot-shaped peninsula that lies in the Mediterranean Sea. To the north of the country are the Alps. The capital of Italy is Rome. Located within the city of Rome is Vatican City. The Vatican is one of the smallest states in the world; in fact, it is simply a small section of Rome. The Vatican is inhabited by the Pope and other church officials who are warmongers and who are antagonistic to the principles of socialism. The Pope is a modern exponent of feudalism and is determined to bring about a third world war. He is an accomplice of the United States and is supported by American capitalists and imperialists who use him in his religious capacity to indoctrinate the masses to submit to their oppressors. The Vatican is an avowed enemy of socialism and the working classes, especially the Soviet Union and its democratic states."

A teacher did not dare to challenge such an answer because it might jeopardize his own position. So the best a good teacher could hope for was to instill as much knowledge as he could and tolerate the redundancy.

Even problems in math had overtones of communistic doctrine. An example of a typical math problem might be: *a kulak* (an owner of private land) has fourteen hens. His allotment for the state co-op is only 1839 eggs per year. A *kolchoz* (commune) is interested in feeding all the people and is much more prosperous, providing the working class with many more eggs. What is the per cent of productivity of 54,395 hens of a *Kolchoz* that produce 8,941,670 eggs to feed the workers?

126

History was even more distasteful and distorted. All a student had to do was to *ad lib* a few choice propaganda phrases and he could get a good grade.

But I remember one incident that didn't turn out the way the student had anticipated.

Standa Teply was the son of a prominent communist of the community. He was not the most intelligent student in the class, but he was among the most apt at improvising an answer.

One day the teacher, Comrade Cikarek, called on Standa to tell us about the Spanish Revolution and General Franco.

Standa usually spent his time in history class catching up on his homework in other subjects so he hadn't bothered to listen to the discussion of the subject a few days earlier. He stood up, his eyes scanning the room for some prompting from his friends. But just at that moment, Comrade Lang, the principal, walked in to observe Comrade Cikarek's method of conducting classes. Comrade Cikarek explained to the principal that Standa had just been called upon to give a résumé of the Spanish Revolution.

"Good," said the principal amiably. "That is one of my favorite topics. Go ahead and continue."

"All right, Standa. Tell us: what was the cause of the Revolution?" the teacher asked solicitously.

Standa faintly remembered that it was a communist revolution, but that was about the extent of his recollection. Improvising had served him well many times before, so he cautiously started, "The suppressed working class in Spain clashed with the capitalists . . . "

The expression on the principal's face remained animated, so he continued, "The reason for the uprising was that the workers had wretched living and working conditions. Factory laborers were underpaid. Long hours—twelve or more a day —were required of them. There was also a lack of machinery, and work was hazardous around what little equipment there

127

was. Such conditions spawned a revolt among the workers . . ." His recital went on and on repeating the phrases he was so dexterous at using.

After a while, even the principal grew tired of hearing his rambling, so he interrupted, "Can you tell us the actual date of the beginning of the Revolution and who was responsible for the uprising?"

Standa tried to save face. He looked around trying to catch a clue from the other students, but they did not dare to coax him. Comrade Cikarek saw it was hopeless so he told Standa to sit down and put a "F" in his notebook for the day's grade.

"Just a minute," interrupted Comrade Lang. "Maybe Standa can tell us about General Franco."

Standa's face fell; he swallowed hard and slowly stammered, "General Franco . . . was an . . . er . . . outstanding Spanish general who . . . er . . . sided with the working class. He . . . er . . . strongly denounced the . . . er . . . traitorous ruling class."

No one commented one way or the other. Without looking at the principal, who was obviously fuming by then, Standa continued on more steadily, "Franco marshalled a large portion of the army which led the working class against the imperialistic oppressors and valiantly fought to free the oppressed."

If he had actually tried, Standa could not have found a more vulnerable spot to wound or to infuriate the principal. The Spanish Revolution was one subject that was very dear to Comrade Lang's heart. He was shocked at the stupidity of one of the students under his direction who could say that Franco was pro-communist. It was the worst possible thing Standa could have said. Like all communists, Comrade Lang deified all communistic heroes; but those who were not with the Party were scornfully railed without mercy. He considered General Franco to be diabolical and proceeded to tell us so in no uncertain terms for the next hour. Besides Franco's alleged faults, we listened to a lecture on the slothfulness of youth; how the younger generation, the hope of the future state of communism, must become aware of its heritage and duties; and whatever else came to his mind.

This incident was particularly amusing to me because it so perfectly illustrated the ineffectiveness of the communist's efforts to genuinely attract young people. By circumstantial influence, Standa should have been a model communist youth, but communist philosophy had simply failed to affect him.

Not long after school began, Comrade Mladenka called on me in class. Instead of asking a question, I was surprised when she inquired, "What's this I hear about your not belonging to the C. S. M.?"

"Jejdanecky, uz to zase zacina," I thought to myself. "I had hoped I could concentrate on studies and forget about the C. S. M., but here we go again."

"You do intend to join, don't you, Peter?" she went on pleasantly.

"No, I don't," I replied resolutely.

"I thought you were interested in going on to higher education. Don't you know that it is the first requisite for college?"

"I was under the impression that good grades were the first requisite for college," I hedged, "and the second condition was to be from the working class. I hope to keep my grades as high as I can, and you know that I certainly fulfill the second requirement."

"That's all well and good, Peter, but you certainly should join the C.S.M. Since you were in the *internat* and factory, it's hard to believe that you're not already a member. Why haven't you joined?" Her tone was polite but very firm.

What was I to say? I had answered the same question so many times before, and every time I answered, I got myself in hot water. I liked school and wanted to stay to finish and later go on to the university. I didn't care to "rock my boat"

129

when things were finally going the way I wanted them to go. So I remained silent.

"Come, come, your tongue isn't tied. Why haven't you joined?"

By that time, all forty students in the class were listening intently to hear what I would say. I was sort of a novelty in the school because I was the only student who didn't "belong." All the rest of the students had joined the youth organization. Some joined solely to stay in school; others joined because they truly believed the teachings of Marx and Lenin. I could feel all eyes turn to me as the blood rose in my face.

"I can never be a communist," I said quietly.

"And why not? I belong to the Party and every other student in this room has joined the youth organization. Since when are you better than the rest of us?" her voice grew rather indignant.

"I don't claim to be better than anyone, Comrade Mladenka. I just can't bring myself to join the Communist Youth Organization. I think it would be like slapping God in the face."

I happened to know that Comrade Mladenka's parents went to Mass every Sunday, and that, in the beginning, she, too, had joined the Party just to be able to finish her education and get a job as a teacher. It was true that in class she taught only what was prescribed, but still she helped to mold young minds by promoting anti-religious teachings. Whether she liked it or not, she was responsible for undermining those students who might have still been loyal to God if she had not exerted her influences.

"If I were a communist, I would eventually have to become an atheist," I ventured ungallantly.

"I know many communists who believe in God and are good members of the Party at the same time. Peter, you know very well that no one will demand that you give up your faith in God."

That argument was well worn by that time. It was one of

130

the recruiting phrases for getting new members and I had heard it a hundred times. It was true that no one would *demand* your rejection of God, but it was also very true that once you were a member, you were expected to work and behave in direct opposition to religious teachings.

"Peter, I didn't know you were so unreasonable. It seems to me you are fanatic on the subject."

"That's funny, whenever someone is not with the communists, he is considered a fanatic. I happen to think that it is not I who am the fanatic," I observed. "Lenin was the one who wrote 'We must make war on religion. That is the A-B-C of materialism," and Marx taught that 'Religion is the opium of the people' and must be destroyed. These statements seem to be those of a fanatic. If I seem like a fanatic, it is because I am deeply concerned to see God insulted at every turn. How can I call myself a child of God and not be disturbed?"

Now I had gone and put my foot in my mouth again. It seemed I could never learn to leave a door open through which I could retreat. But somehow when that particular subject came up, I could not be prudent enough to remain silent. Believe me, so many, many times I had wrestled within myself with the problem of whether there could ever be a reconciliation between my belief in God and membership in the C. S. M. But every single time, I came up with the same answer—the two are incompatible. I could not yield.

I did not know how Comrade Mladenka would take my bluntness, and so I was surprised when she called me aside about a week later and said, "Peter, do you know that the principal knows about our discussion?"

"I'm not surprised."

"I felt I must tell him myself so that he would get the story straight. He wanted to dismiss you at once, but I told him that I would take full responsibility for you. I'm sticking my neck out for you, so please, don't do anything more to get me in trouble."

I think Comrade Mladenka genuinely believed that eventually she could get me to change to her viewpoint. Once I overheard her tell another teacher that she believed any standards could be changed if given the right environment and enough time. "Take the diamond as an example," she had told the teacher, "once it was only carbon. Given enough time and the right condition, it became the hardest substance known. These boys and girls are very much like that."

A few days after her warning, a meeting of all the students was called immediately after school. Because it was a C. S. M. meeting, I went home as soon as classes were dismissed.

The next morning on my way to school, my friend Vojta made it a point to sit beside me in the bus.

"Peter, have you heard what happened at the meeting yesterday?" he asked.

"No, I went straight home from school."

"You should have been there; you were the topic of most of the meeting," Vojta announced excitedly.

"Me? What did I do?"

"Do you know Lida Tucek?"

"No. I can't remember even hearing the name."

"Well, it seems Lida knows about you. She stood up at the meeting and questioned the admission of a student who refuses to join the C. S. M. She suggested that your presence be brought before the school trustees for investigation. She said she considered the admission of anyone opposed to Marx and Lenin a perverted judgment and suggested that the officers of the youth organization hold a closed session and demand an explanation."

"Yeah, I seem to have knack for stirring up trouble," I groaned.

I asked Vojta to arrange some way so that I could see Lida without it being too obvious that I was curious about observing her. He suggested that I meet him near the chemistry lab during the first class break. Lida would have to pass that way for her next class. We made a pretense of looking

132

for the soccer coach as an excuse for being in that part of the corridor. As we spoke to the coach, Vojta's eyes indicated the girl to me.

"So that's Lida Tucek," I thought. "She doesn't look the way I expected her to. In fact, she's very pretty."

I had expected Lida to look very plain, but she was a vivacious girl of average height, with long, dark brown hair that softly framed a lovely face. Her whole countenance was striking, even her walk was regal.

After school that afternoon, Lida and a friend were waiting for me at the door. They stopped me and introduced themselves. "This is my friend, Ruzka Skopik," Lida said. "She is the vice-president of the C. S. M. My name is Lida Tucek. I understand you don't belong to the youth organization. The working class . . ."

"Look, don't preach any sermons to me about the working class," I interrupted. "I worked in the factory for a long time before I came here and I believe I happen to have a good deal more first hand knowledge about the working class than you. As for the C. S. M., I don't belong now, and I don't ever intend to. Right now, I've got a bus to catch."

I had been curt with Lida because I knew that she was just repeating the same old fabrications that were so odious to me. I didn't know how she would react; but if she were offended, she would probably go to the principal, and he would call me in for an explanation.

I decided that I didn't wish to incur her wrath again so I made sure there was plenty of distance between Lida and me.

Shortly after school started the next fall, it was announced that groups were being organized for the *Spartakiada* which was planned for the following July. The *Spartakiada* has an old tradition that goes back many generations. Originally called *Slet,* it is a kind of intra-olympics that are held every four years to exhibit the accomplishments of Czech athletes in gymnastics and calisthenics. Usually, the *Spartakiada* is

133

held in *Strohovsky stadion*, the huge stadium in Praha, where groups from every district are dressed alike and perform in co-ordinated rhythm. It is a very popular event and draws crowds from all Czechoslovakia. The communists continue to hold the *Spartakiada* every four years and use so great a gathering as another means to glorify communism. Each school, factory, *internat*, and even the army is ordered to send representatives. Our school was ordered to send the *Czech Beseda*, the colorful folk dances that also have very old traditions. The costumes of both the boys and girls are elaborately embroidered in a design that indicates the district the dancers are from. Usually the girls spend the free time of an entire winter or more making the lace and embroidering the costumes for themselves and their brothers or boy friend.

Comrade Mladenka called me aside and said, "Peter, since you won't join the C. S. M. you should do something to show that you are willing to participate in school activities. Even though you are on the soccer team, it would still be wise for you to join the folk dancing group to show your good will. You will be wearing our provincial dance costume instead of a uniform. Anyway, I'd like for you to join as a favor to me."

"I suppose I could wear my uncle's costume," I mused. "All right, Comrade Mladenka, I'll be there." At least I owed her my cooperation for what she was doing for me, but I wasn't anxious to join. I just couldn't abide the constant regulations that were prescribed for everyone in everything— even dancing and sports. I wanted to be and to act like an individual, to go and to do the things that appealed to me personally, and not always to follow some decree from some commissar. But I had told Comrade Mladenka I would join the dance group and so I did.

For some reason, I was a little late for the first practice. Comrade Mladenka was the instructor of the group and she had Lida in front of the class, showing them a certain turn.

134

She looked up and saw me enter. "I'm glad you're here, Peter. We are short a partner. Step in here and be Lida's partner."

There was a moment of awkward silence. I didn't know what to do. I certainly didn't want to be Lida's partner because I had been purposely avoiding any more trouble with her. Lida seemed a little ill at ease, too. But I soon found that Lida was not only nice looking, she was an excellent dancer.

"This dance class is turning out all right after all," I thought. To Lida I said, "Where did you learn to dance?"

"I took dancing lessons," she replied.

"You must have had a good teacher."

"This isn't the first time you've danced, either," she said with just the right hint of coquettishness.

"Yes, sir, this dancing is much better than I thought it would be. She's quite a girl," I speculated to myself.

Other dance practices went on as well and I began to look forward to them. I was taking a fancy to Lida and she seemed to be returning my interest.

A few months later, she said teasingly, "You know something, Peter?" She tossed her head slightly and her dark hair fell in cascade over her shoulder. She had eyes that literally sparkled and a way of looking at you as though you were the only person in the room. Among her many other attributes, she was also blessed with a silver tongue. "The first time we talked, I never dreamed I'd ever be dancing with you; for that matter, I didn't even care to."

"No, I don't suppose you did. Do you regret the change?"

"Quite the contrary. I like dancing with you very much."

"Thank you, Lida, I'm enjoying every minute that I'm with you." And I meant every word I said. Over the next several months, I made a point of seeing Lida at school and at dance practice as often as I could, and our attraction for each other grew.

135

Vojta and I usually rode to school on the bus together and often shared confidences. One morning I told him of my growing interest in Lida.

"I'm surprised at you, Peter," he commented rather astounded.

"Why? Lida is a very nice girl."

"Certainly she is. But I'm surprised you picked the daughter of a member of the S. T. B. to become interested in."

"The S. T. B.! Are you sure her father works for the S. T. B.?" It was my turn to be astounded.

"Yes, I'm positive," Vojta assured me. "I've seen him go to the S. T. B. office several times and Luzka Skopik also told me that Lida's father works there."

I had not known it. Although I couldn't forget, I didn't let her father's position dampen our good times.

The price of a movie was very small, because the movies were used as another way to propagandize, and the price was kept exceptionally low so that the people could afford to go. I had a little money saved so I summoned enough courage to invite Lida to a movie, and she graciously accepted.

Because I had to come from Hradsko on the bus, and the movie started only a few minutes after the bus arrived, we agreed to meet at the bus station in Zamky. When I stepped off the bus, Lida was waiting for me. I had never seen her looking so radiant. Certainly she was pretty in her ordinary dress at school, but that night, she was exceptionally breathtaking. She wore a white dress and high heels. Her hair was fixed in a most becoming way that seemed to make her face glow. She was truly beautiful.

The movie we saw was about Dr. Jansky, the noted scientist who discovered the different blood factors. We had a very pleasant evening together. After the movie we walked through the town for awhile, laughing and talking of different things. Lida told me of her little brother, but didn't mention the rest of her family. In fact, the whole time I

136

knew Lida, she never once spoke of her family, other than her little brother.

I saw Lida fairly often after that. Different boys and girls told me that her enthusiasm in the C. S. M. was gone and that she didn't even go to all the meetings any longer. They said that she even started to go to Mass on Sundays, but Lida herself never mentioned anything about her private life.

One day during a class break, a girl, who called herself a friend of Lida's, came up to me and asked if I wanted to hear something interesting.

"I always like to hear something interesting, Eva," I replied.

Eva brought out a letter she had hidden inside her notebook and began to read:

My dear Lida,

I am sorry I did not get to see you when I was in Zamky last week. I had to get back here to Brno as soon as possible to take care of some important matters so I was not able to wait until you returned from your outing.

While I was there, I was able to see the principal of your school. I am most disturbed with his report of you. He said that it is evident that there has been a change in you lately—not just the natural change of a girl your age, but your whole attitude is different. Comrade Lang told me that you no longer have any interest in the youth organization and that you do not even go to all of their meetings. I could hardly believe what he said, but he assured me that it is true. Most disturbing of all, he said you have started to go to Mass.

Need I remind you, Lida, that your whole future may very well depend on what you do today. Be practical and go along with the youth organization so that you will never rue this time of life. Most of all, stop this silly foolishness of going to church immediately. Think of what you are doing. Here I am working for the govern-

*ment, and my own daughter goes to church. You put
me in a very awkward position. You know that going
to church is highly frowned upon and your actions are
recorded on your* cadre *card and also on mine.*

*So I am telling you as emphatically as I can to get
back into the work of the youth organization and become a credit to yourself and to me. I expect you to
comply with my wishes.*

Lovingly,
Your Father

"Where did you get that, Eva?" I asked when she finished
reading.

"I found it on the floor near Lida's locker."

"Why did Lida's father write her a letter when he lives in
the same house and sees her every day?"

"Why, Peter," Eva said curiously, "I thought you knew.
Didn't Lida ever tell you that her parents are divorced? Her
mother is remarried. The man who works for the S. T. B.
is not her real father—that's her stepfather. Her real father
works for the government in Brno."

I was surprised at what Eva told me. Lida had never mentioned anything about her family to me, and yet her father's
letter bothered me more than I cared to admit. I wondered
whether Lida would take his advice and resume her activity
in the C. S. M. or not. I thought that her silence might possibly be a sign that she was following her father's advice, but
I was never sure. Anyway, her father's views were exactly
opposite from mine and the fact that he was her father would
certainly have a strong influence on her.

St. Nicholas Day approached. I tried to think of a gift to
give Lida that would especially please her. I finally decided
on a book of poems. I noted that a particular edition had her
favorite poem in it. My sister wrapped my gift and I put it
into the box of gifts that were to be distributed by "St.
Nicholas" at the school party.

Lida beamed as she opened her gift.

To my surprise, Lida also gave me a book. It was a biography of Dr. Jansky. I was complimented that she remembered the movie we saw together and chose to remind me of our first date in that way.

It was the following Saturday before I had time to read my book. I found a quiet place in my room and began to read. I felt sure I would enjoy it since Lida had picked it for me. The story was the same as the movie, and I enjoyed it very much. The story of Dr. Jansky ended as the movie had, but there was still half of the book left. I anticipated more of the life of Dr. Jansky but found, instead, that the second half had a completely different story. I became suspicious when I began reading and found it was about the Communist Revolution. I checked the author and was amazed to find he was a noted communist.

I didn't know what to think. Had Lida been tricked when she bought the book and thought it was only the story of Dr. Jansky, or was she subtly trying to sneak some communistic propaganda to me? I couldn't be sure.

It irritated me that I became suspicious of Lida so easily. And yet, I could not believe, without at least a suggestion of doubt, that she had not thumbed through the book and noticed the two distinct stories and the communist author of the second part.

Actually I was more hurt than irritated. I had been harassed from so many sides in junior high, the *internats,* the factory, and in high school, but none of those antagonisms had hurt me so keenly as Lida's actions. Lida must have known that I was most fond of her. She had certainly made me believe that she was devoted to me. So quite naturally I had expected that Lida, at least, would understand my disposition and not pique me more. I had tried to understand her secrecy about her family and her actions, but somehow there was always a nagging doubt. Then, to add insult to injury, her book with the communist line made me positive that I could never trust her completely. Even my youthful dreams of Lida were shattered. If I could not be sure of Lida, perhaps I could not be sure of other friends either. I felt terribly frustrated.

Mother sensed that something was wrong although she had no way of knowing what it was. She came into my room that night after I had gone to bed and sat down beside me.

"Peta," she said tenderly, "I am very concerned about you because I know that something is troubling you. I won't ask you to tell me what it is. You are a young man now and need to work out your problems for yourself. Don't be too disappointed at whatever happened to make you feel this way. But just remember that you are still so very young and have so much ahead of you. Your life is only beginning. When you graduate, you will be only twenty. If things go well for you, perhaps you may be able to go to the university. But don't set your goals too high. Live each day as it is, and be thankful for whatever blessings come your way. Don't be too impatient to achieve manhood. It will come—slowly and perhaps painfully—but it will come. Just be a man that you yourself can be proud to be. You will almost certainly be called upon to make many terribly hard decisions and sacrifices, but I'm sure you can and will do whatever is asked of you. I pray someday your father and I will both be proud of the man you are."

Mother bent down and kissed my forehead as she had done so many times before when I was younger. She then silently left the room.

After that I lay awake a long time. She was right, of course. There was still so much I wanted in life. But even if I were allowed to go to the university, there was still no guarantee that I could get a job which I liked or which paid well—no matter what kind of degree I earned. We all knew of highly specialized professional men who worked as common laborers and who barely existed financially. I was impatient to reach maturity and to take my place in life. I wanted to make some-

140

thing of myself, but I knew it was almost impossible under the existing conditions.

Life dominated by the atheistic communists was becoming even more unbearable. Their presence was everywhere. I felt I was slowly being suffocated.

The old haunting idea of escape kept coming back more incessantly.

"I will never be cowed," I promised myself. "Certainly I want to be a man. But I want to be a free man. A man who can make free decisions and breathe free air."

That night I made up my mind that I would definitely try to escape no matter what the odds or the risks might be.

14. STALIN IS DEAD

"Stalin is dead," exclaimed Anynka, my sister, as she burst into my room.

Needless to say, I was stunned by her announcement. I had just been studying a Czech language lesson that extolled Stalin as being *the* linguist of all time. In every subject in school, we were taught that Stalin was the personification of knowledge in every science. He was alleged to be the world's greatest hero, statesman, thinker, military strategist, and he was even called "the engineer of human souls." "We don't need to think; Comrade Stalin is thinking for us" was the tendency of thought among his followers in those days. To them, Stalin was a virtual god on earth.

In spite of such deification of Stalin, before me, gleefully dancing upon hearing of his death, was a fourteen year old school girl who had Stalin's "virtues" drummed into her head every school day of her life.

Around and around she twirled repeating again and again, "Stalin is dead; Stalin is dead . . ." I had not seen her so jubilant for a long time.

"Who told you so?" I inquired with great excitement.

"I just heard it on the radio," Anynka stopped her dancing long enough to say breathlessly. "I was washing dishes and listening to polkas when they interrupted the music with the announcement. They said, 'Moscow just announced the sad news that Generalissimo Stalin is dead. Stay tuned for further details.' Oh, Peta, Stalin is dead!"

Breathlessly, she dashed from my room and ran outside to tell my parents. I followed her as far as the kitchen so that I could listen to the radio and hear the news myself. As I entered the kitchen, the radio blared, ". . . further details

142

about his untimely death will be announced as soon as they are made available from *Tass*." Then there was serious music,

So it was true! The immortal was dead. The indestructible was gone. It was incredible. Ever since the end of the war, and especially ever since the communists took over, all we ever heard from the communists was praise for Stalin: Stalin was the one who had won the war; he was the one whom we all depended upon to provide happiness for us; he was a god. And now the god was dead—just like every other mortal.

I suppose the thoughts that flashed through almost everyone's mind when they heard the news was: What will happen now? Will his death change things for us? For the world? Who will replace him?

I will never forget that afternoon. Further study was out of the question. I wanted to be alone and to think—to think and to try to comprehend what the consequences of his death would have upon us.

In the evening I set out on a long walk through the forest near my village. Soon the moon came up very big and bright. To me even the sky looked freshly cleansed, as though a haze or impurity had been removed. The temperature was freezing, making conditions ideal for meditation. From the distance, I could hear the barking of dogs. Under me my every step on the frozen snow echoed sharply. The wind through the bare trees made them crack and squeak. Everything about that night was poignant and invigorating.

Death usually has a sobering effect, but not on March 5, 1953. The news of Stalin's death brought a sense of relief and anticipation.

Even though we had been thoroughly indoctrinated as to his "greatness," we did not believe these lies. How could any man who claimed to be good keep prisons and concentration camps full of innocent people? How could a just man condemn his fellow-man to death without a trial just because of his political or religious convictions? No, Stalin was not a god, nor was he good. One good look around us was more

143

than enough to accuse and convict Stalin as a blood-thirsty dictator who had seized absolute power in the Communist Party and used it as a means of furthering his own warped ambitions and of liquidating any personal opposition. Although Stalin vehemently claimed to despise the sovereignty of the Czars, he had created a dictatorial empire far more terrible than any Czar.

He was not *our* countryman, but his decisions and obsessions determined our destinies. The couple who lived across the street from us had a son of twenty-one who had been sentenced to life imprisonment for underground anti-communistic activities. Even within my own family were two relatives who had served terms in concentration camps. In truth we all were living in a gigantic concentration camp. Our whole country was encircled by barbed wire and was guarded by a special branch of the army called *Pohranicni straz*. For the most part, the soldiers of this branch were devoted members of the Communist Party. They patroled the borders with guns, dogs, and manned machine gun towers, making escape almost impossible.

It is significant that we, like all the other countries of the communist bloc, including Russia herself, had not come under the communist domain by a free election, but rather by stealth and treachery. Although historically Czechoslovakia had been a democratic country, we had been betrayed into slavery, and the yoke of bondage weighed heavily upon us. All these things went through my mind, but the big question that remained unanswered at that time was: What now?

In school the entire next day was dedicated to speeches about Stalin's "bravery" and his "greatness." Until his funeral, which was a state spectacle, wakes were held in every city, town, and village with a huge crepe-draped picture of Stalin dominating the "altar" which was banked with flowers and torches. Special guards, made up of Party members, ordinary citizens, students, soldiers, and school children were ordered to guard this "altar." It was to have been a time of great mourning, but the expressions on the faces of most of the "mourners" betrayed their true feelings.

I particularly remember seeing Marka's brother. He, too, had been pressed into guarding Stalin's "altar." When I caught his eye, he grimaced, mimicking pain, then winked his eye as his expression changed to a bitter sneer.

An official delegation of Czechoslovakian officials attended Stalin's funeral in Moscow. As it happened, the Czechoslovakian president, Klement Gottwald, was fatally striken in Moscow and died a few days later.

Again there was national mourning with parades and more eulogies.

With the death of two dignitaries of such magnitude we really hoped and expected that there would be great changes for the better. But nothing really changed. Antonin Zapotocky, a top communist became president of Czechoslovakia and continued the policies of his predecessor.

We learned that the situation was different in Russia. Immediately following Stalin's death a triumvirate, made up of Malenkov, Molotov and Beria, assumed power. But within a year, Beria, who was head of the N. K. V. D. (secret police), was denounced and executed as a traitor. Soon Malenkov was deposed as Premier. Instead of being executed, he was exiled to Siberia as a director of an electrical power plant where he was rendered powerless in the national struggle.

From the strife that ensued within Russia, the names of Nikita Khrushchev and N. A. Bulganin gradually began to emerge as the most powerful, with Khrushchev eventually getting the upper hand and the control of power.

On the surface, at least, it seemed that there was a new, more lenient spirit that flowed through Russia. The people of Czechoslovakia, however, did not feel the thaw. The old Stalinists were imbedded too deeply to be ousted by the new Russian leaders, and consequently, were able to retain their power in Czechoslovakia.

It wasn't until February, 1956, when the communists held

145

their Twentieth Congress of the Russian Communist Party, that Stalin was unveiled as the homicidal maniac that he actually was.

Before the entire Congress of the Communist Party and in the most fiery language possible. Khrushchev denounced Stalin as a murderer, a pathological liar, a fraud, a perverter of Marx-Leninism. Khrushchev gave specific names, revealing Stalin as the instigator of mass terror and annihilation, as the deporter of entire populations, as the forger of false evidence against alleged enemies, as the coward in World War II, and as the possessor of diabolical vanity that would stop at nothing to further egotism.

Naturally, such a devastating speech was not made public immediately, but we heard about it later from foreign radio stations, such as the B.B.C., Voice of America, and Radio Free Europe, as soon as copies of the speech leaked to the free world.

The publication of the speech caused great confusion within the Communist Party. No Party member was certain he would retain his position any longer, and they all seemed to be jockeying for power.

Because there was much uncertainty at that time, there was some hope that even I would be accepted in the university. At the urging of Comrade Mladenka, I applied in a chemistry college because it had the most vacancies. Chemistry was not really the field I wanted, but I stood a better chance of being accepted there.

Actually, I didn't care too much if I were accepted or rejected by the university. My decision to escape was definitely taking shape. But I had made such a commotion about getting accepted into high school, that I had to at least pretend that I wanted to further my studies in order to allay any suspicion of secretly making other plans. I needed time—time enough to find out as much as I possibly could about the Iron Curtain. While I waited for word from the college, I tried to act as though the only thing I had on my mind was graduation and college.

The repercussions of the Twentieth Congress of the Russian Communist Party became more and more apparent as time went on. Before Khrushchev's speech, it was a great "crime" to even intimate anything derogatory against Stalin or anyone under his patronage. Then suddenly people began to say publicly the things that would have previously sent them to long prison terms.

One morning when I came to school, my classmate, Bohus, was just elated. "Have you heard the latest, Peter? Olga Lepeshinskaja was a swindler."

"Who said so?" I asked unbelievingly. I had never heard anyone say anything that was considered as seditious as that in public, so I tried to evade him.

"It was on the news this morning on the Praha station," he persisted.

"Are you sure?" I inquired cautiously.

"Certainly I'm sure. I heard it myself," Bohus declared. He was not really a true communist even though he belonged to the youth organization. Bohus was just one of those who kept his mouth shut and did whatever he was told because he did not care to get involved in any kind of trouble. As each student came into the room, Bohus rushed to announce what he had heard.

We had never heard such talk before, so naturally we had a very animated discussion before classes started. Everyone agreed that Lepeshinskaja had just ridden the wave of Stalin's popularity, and when he was denounced, many others who had achieved fame under him were also discredited.

Shortly after classes started, the principal came into our room. He was obviously very disturbed.

"Comrades, I am ashamed of you," he scowled. "I have just been told about the scandalous gossip that is circulating around this school. How can you believe anything like this?"

147

We students began to squirm uncomfortably as Comrade Lang paced the floor wringing his hands in anxiety.

"Don't you know that you can't believe the lies that the Voice of America and Radio Free Europe broadcast? They will do anything to undermine your faith in our new socialist society. These Western radio stations are sponsored by capitalists who are jealous of our achievements and will use every insidious and unscrupulous means to bring about the destruction of the paradise that we are building. Their propaganda is poisonous. Never listen to these stations so as not to become infected by them. And furthermore," he admonished, "don't believe all that you hear from those in our own midst." He turned and faced me squarely as he scowled. "There are some among you who try to help the Western imperialists to destroy us. They would destroy your morals and your faith in the great Soviet Union which is still our shining example and our guide in achieving perfect communism."

It was apparent that he thought I was the one who had spread the story of Lepeshinskaja, and he thought I had got it from Radio Free Europe or the Voice of America. I wanted to clear up his mistaken idea once and for all, so I raised my hand.

"Yes, Comrade Esterka?" He wasn't too eager to recognize me.

"Sir, I understand that it was not a Western radio station that announced that Lepeshinskaja was discredited. Bohus heard it on the Praha station on the 7 o'clock news."

Comrade Lang obviously did not believe me so he started to question Bohus. Bohus readily admitted that he had indeed heard it on a Czech station.

Dismayed and embarrassed, Comrade Lang turned to the teacher, Mr. Vesely.

"Yes, it's true," Mr. Vesely assured him. "I heard it, too. Lepeshinskaja was not the only scientist they mentioned, even Lysenko and his theory were discredited."

It must have given Mr. Vesely a great deal of pleasure

148

to be the one to openly tell Comrade Lang of the Russian scientists' fall. He was an elderly man who had been a good teacher for many years, but he knew the only way he could keep his job was to keep his opinions to himself. Only once when he and I were alone, did I see him give vent to his true feelings.

It happened during my first year in high school when the whole school was practicing for the parade which was to be held on May Day, the communist workers' holiday. The principal had noticed me among the rest of the student body and had sent me back to school. He had reported that I didn't belong among "these progressive youths who are the future of communism." So I gladly went back to the school and reported to Mr. Vesely as the principal had directed me to do. Mr. Vesely had asked me to help him clean the chemistry laboratory. The whole time I had helped him, he fumed and fretted about the regime and the deplorable working conditions for teachers.

If the principal thought I would be disappointed not to be able to march in the parade, he was mistaken. He was really doing me a favor because it was a severe penance for me to march behind communist banners and flags. Most people felt the same way. Whenever there was some sort of parade or celebration, the people from every factory, school and organization were ordered to participate. If they didn't, it was noted on their *cadre card*.

These parades were actually a composite of the entire society in which we lived. At the head of the parade, carrying flags, banners, and propaganda slogans, arrogantly marched a few pompous Party members who were drunk with power and self-importance. Following them were the disgruntled masses who were forced to march, walking with down-cast eyes and with long, scowling faces, hating even to be seen. It was quite a sight.

Even the floats in these parades were used as propaganda against the West, the Pope, or Wall Street. Usually the United

States bore the brunt of the communists' contempt. Often a float would represent the "bloody American capitalist and imperialist" with a caricature of Uncle Sam sitting on an atom bomb holding a facsimile of dollar bills in one hand and the American flag in the other. Even though the American flag was displayed for ridicule, the average person scanned to see it as it went by. It was the bright spot of the parade for us because this was the only time we could see the American flag, the symbol of a free country and the freedom for which we so desperately yearned.

In my own determination to be free, I kept my eyes and ears open to everything that concerned the border or the experiences of those who had actually seen the Iron Curtain. From Radio Free Europe, I learned that barbed and electric wires completely encircled Czechoslovakia, and that in some places there were mine fields. There were special programs interviewing those who escaped in which the escapees told how they had eluded the guards. By that time, not many people escaped. Probably many more tried, but only a few were successful. Some of them were shot; others were caught and punished.

I vaguely knew one of those who was caught. He was Milan Vorel, a schoolmate, who was in the class below me. His father had been a prominent medical doctor who was ousted as head of a department of a large hospital because of his religious and political convictions. Milan was outstanding in chemistry, but was not accepted in the high school in his hometown, therefore, he was compelled to work in a factory. After a year or so, he was accepted in our school, which was a great distance from his home. He had done as Mr. Prikryl had once advised me, "Go to school far away from your home town where nobody knows you or your family."

Milan had to walk across town from the railroad station to school each morning. As soon as classes were over, he had

150

to rush back to the station. Therefore, I never had a chance to know him well. However, the main reason I had never gotten to know Milan better was that he, too, had refused to join the C. S. M. after he learned that I had not been expelled the previous year. (During first year at high school, I was the only student who did not join the C. S. M.; the next year, four more refused to join; and the third year, there were eleven students who were not permitted to march in the May Day parade because they did not "belong.") Those of us who were not members of the C. S. M. did not associate with each other very much, because we did not want anyone to think we were trying to create some sort of gang or organization of our own. It was up to each one of us to fight our own battles in our own way—alone.

Everyone suspected that something had happened to Milan since he had not been in school for a long while. Although there was much conjecture about him, no one was positive of what had happened.

I learned the facts of Milan's misfortune from Comrade Mladenka at a pre-graduation party. While we danced, she asked me suddenly, "Peter, what do you think about Milan's rash venture?"

I was so surprised at the directness of her question, I didn't know what to say. Finally, I stammered, "I don't know what to think. I just heard that he tried to escape."

"Did you know about his plans?" She seemed to be very interested in my reply.

"No, I didn't. I hardly knew Milan at all. But his classmates said that he seemed to know more about chemistry than the teacher."

"What do you think of the whole escapade?" she persisted.

I had to be very careful in answering her. If I became flustered, she might correctly suspect that I was already laying the groundwork for my escape, and she would certainly report her suspicions. I tried to act very nonchalant when I replied, "He was bound to have known the risks involved. I thought he had more sense than to go near the forbidden territory."

"Oh, he was not so close to the border," Comrade Mladenka explained. "They caught him in Znojmo."

Znojmo is a large town fairly near the border but it is not located within the forbidden territory which is the territory adjacent to the border which is zealously guarded.

"How can that be? Znojmo is an ordinary town just like every other town," I theorized.

"Yes, but it is close enough to the border and some of the trains from there go through the *Pohranicni pasmo* (border territory). The border guards watch these trains very carefully. They must have suspected Milan because they arrested him just as he boarded a train which was headed for the forbidden territory. They searched his belongings and found some things which indicated he was trying to escape."

"What did they find?"

"I don't know, probably some wire cutters or something. Anyway, he later confessed that he was planning to escape into Austria."

I was not surprised that Milan confessed. Fictitious confessions had been obtained from seemingly invincible men, so it could not have been too hard to get a confession from a mere boy.

"How do you know all this?" I wondered aloud.

"The police told the principal," she explained.

The conversation trailed off at that point and we danced in silence. I thought of Milan and wondered where he was at that moment. I could imagine how disappointed he must have been, not just because he was caught, but because his whole life was completely ruined. Because Milan was only seventeen when he was arrested, and because he wasn't actually in the act of escaping at the time he was arrested, he probably would get only a few years in prison for his "crime." But what then? He could never finish school or get a good job. His *cadre card* would always bear the stigma of "a traitor

152

of the working class; a deserter; one who is to be destroyed."

"Peter, would you do something like Milan did?" Comrade Mladenka broke the silence.

"What do you mean?"

"Does she suspect something or is she just making conversation?" My heart seemed to skip a beat.

"Would you like to escape?" she was very persistent in her questioning.

What could I answer? I couldn't help but wonder what she would say if I told her the truth—that I had already decided to go and had been mentally testing every scheme I could think of. I didn't want to lie so I replied with complete honesty, "I don't see how anyone would *want* to leave the home and family they love and go to a foreign country where they don't know anyone or even the language. It certainly wouldn't be easy."

"That's right," she agreed as I took her back to her seat at the end of the dance set.

Hearing of Milan's misfortune dampened my hopes somewhat, but I was still determined to try, and I continued to keep my eyes and ears open for any information that might help me.

A good bit of useful information came to me from an old man who was a guest at the wedding of one of my relatives. During the dinner the conversation somehow turned to a recent experience he had had at the border. The old man told us the following story:

"I leased some public land to make hay from the grass. As you all know, each section of public land is numbered and you bid on the tract by number without seeing the tract. As it happened, the sections of grass I bought were very near the border. When I went to mow it, I noticed a sign on the road between the meadows that said: 'Border Territory —To Enter Without Permission Is Strictly Forbidden.' I was in hurry to get through making my hay so I ignored the sign and kept going. But I didn't get very far before two

153

soldiers stopped me and asked to see my permission.

'I don't have any permission,' I told them. 'I just want to cut the grass that I leased.'

'Did you see the sign the soldiers asked?'

'Sure.'

'Can you read?'

I looked at the soldiers not knowing if they were joking or not. But both of them were very serious. It gave me a funny feeling to stand before two men with guns pointed straight at me.

'Sure I can read. What do you think? I'm not stupid,' I answered.

'Well, if you're so smart then, you'll come along with us.'

'Look,' I tried to convince them, 'I'm losing time standing here talking. All I want to do is to mow the grass. Nobody told me I had to have a permission to do that.'

'Well, you know it now, one of the soldiers told me in no uncertain terms. Now just turn around and let's go.'

I jumped on my bicycle, but the soldiers hollered at me to halt.

'Look, man, don't make any trouble or we will use these,' and he indicated his gun.

I realized that I had to obey them, but I played stupid, and said, I'll go slowly on the bike so you can stay with me. Or tell me where to go and I'll wait for you there.

'Don't get smart with us and start walking. The soldier shoved me with his gun.'

We walked about two miles before we came to a small village where the soldiers took me to their command office. It was not easy to convince them that I just went to mow the grass. They asked many questions about my family and me. When I said over and over that my only purpose was to cut the grass, they finally called my hometown to check my *cadre card* and ask questions about my family to see if I lied to them.

'O.K.' the officer finally said, 'you can go now. But come

154

back tomorrow, and we will give you the written permission.'

It was already late in the afternoon when the officer came to such a "favorable" conclusion, so I didn't insist on cutting grass anymore. I was more tired that evening than I would have been if I had worked hard all day.

Early the next morning I went to the officer's office for my permission, but I had to wait about an hour before they gave it to me. It was just a form with a seal and signature saying that I could go to the border area to make hay. But my difficulties didn't end with the permission. Just in the middle of the meadow, there was another sign. This one said: 'Attention! Forbidden Territory. We Will Shoot Without Warning.' You can be sure that this time I was more careful. I realized they were not just joking. I saw the soldiers were watching me all the time as though they thought I was trying to escape."

"Was it very far from the border?" I interrupted the old man.

"I don't know."

"Well, did you see some wires or something around there?"

"No. Not from where I was cutting that day. All I saw were the guards. Two of them were always together. Some of them rode horses and some of them just walked. But those on foot had vicious looking dogs with them."

"How often did they change the guards?" I persisted.

The old man looked at me suspiciously and said, "Listen, why are you so curious? Don't get any silly ideas to go over the hill."

"Oh, no. What do you think? I'm not crazy. I'm just curious, that's all," I tried to convince the old man and also all of those who were listening to the story.

"Ja, it is always good to know how secure we are in this big concentration camp," someone said bitterly.

"I wonder whom they are guarding so carefully," another said sarcastically. "Is it those who are trying escape, or the American imperialists who don't have anything to eat in the

155

United States, so they could come to steal from the table of the working class?"

"You know very well what the idea is," rejoined someone else, "it's to stop the imperialists from penetrating into Czechoslovakia."

"Ja, and meanwhile shoot everyone who gets capitalistic notions, and is not willing to live under the protection of the working class anymore," the satire continued.

I was relieved when the talk became so light.

"Stop the sarcasm and let him finish his story," the man next to me said.

"Did you cut the grass in the forbidden territory, too?" someone asked.

"Yes, I did. Going home that evening, I stopped at the command office again and told the officer that I was supposed to go into the forbidden territory because about half my lease was in it."

" 'O. K.' said the officer. 'Come tomorrow morning and I'll give you helpers.' He raised his eyebrows and noted my reaction. He had a peculiar look in his eyes.

" 'I don't need helpers. All I need is the permission,' I insisted.

" 'We don't give permission for that space. But don't worry. Just come here in the morning and I'll take care of you.'

"So the next morning when I went to the office, the officer made a phone call and in a little while two soldiers with a dog and sub-machine guns came.

" 'Now you can go,' said the officer. 'They have orders to protect you while you work.'

"I'll tell you, it was a funny feeling to be followed all day by guards with a dog that could eat you up. One of the soldiers stayed very close to me while the one with the dog stayed between me and the border."

"Did those same two soldiers stay with you all day?" someone asked.

"Oh, no, they were replaced three times during the day."

"Could you see any wires or anything from where you worked that day?" I could not control my curiosity. This man had a wealth of knowledge that I needed.

"Yes, I could see some wires. They were pretty far from me, and I didn't have a chance to get a very close look at them, but I could see that there were three separate rows of fences. And I also saw two machine gun towers."

"How far were they from each other?" I hoped no one was getting suspicious. I tried to pretend that I was just youthfully curious. Everyone seemed to be more concerned with the man's story and the food in front of them than they were with an inquisitive youth.

"I don't know exactly, but I would say they were close enough so that the guards could see what was going on between them very well."

One of the other listeners joined the conversation. "Were you not scared being under their gun sights all day? Suppose one of your guards would have thought that you were a traitor of our working class and that you wanted to escape?" he jested.

"It's easy to joke about it today, but it was not so funny for me then. Just when I cut the last few yards of grass, something happened that almost scared me to death. To this day I'm not sure what happened, but I probably hit something on the ground, because when I cut the last row, rockets started going up all around me. I dropped the scythe and ran away from there as fast as I could. Even the soldier who stayed close to me started to run at first, but then he fell flat on the ground."

"How far did you run?"

"Not very far because that ferocious dog knocked me down and laid his front paws on my chest. I could feel his hot breath on my face. I'll tell you, I was terrified. I'm sure he would have chewed me up if the soldier had not been there to call him off. It was the only time I was glad that the soldiers were near," he concluded.

157

Not long before graduation, Comrade Mladenka came to me and said, "I'm sorry, Peter, but your application for chemistry college was not accepted. They have had too many applications, and yours has not been accepted."

Since I didn't have my heart set on the chemistry college anyway, I wasn't too disappointed. "That's O.K., I suppose. But are there any other openings for me?"

"Not many. About the only things left are a few openings in the agriculture or the mechanical schools."

"Would you try to see if I can get into the mechanical school?" I tried to seem genuinely concerned even though I didn't have any real interest in mechanics. If I could convince everyone that I really wanted to go to college, it would dispel any suspicion.

"Very well, I'll try. But you should change your selective subject. Should I re-schedule your chemistry period to physics?" Comrade Mladenka asked.

"Please do," I replied even though I realized that I would really have to buckle down and study to be ready to take a physics examination. But I didn't care if my grade would probably be low—just so I graduated.

Other changes that came about right before graduation were the answers we had learned from the Czech and Russian language books that concerned Stalin as being a great linguist. History books were also changed deleting all mention of the "greatness" of Stalin. The biology books completely ignored Lepeshinskaja and Lysenko. Previously the books had extolled Stalin to the sky, but since the denouncement of him, all reference to him was omitted.

Shortly after graduation, I had to go to Brno to take the entrance examination for the mechanical college. I passed the exam and was accepted. I began to make tentative plans to go to college in the fall if my escape plans had not materialized by then.

During the summer vacation, I worked in the factory again, but I spent all my free time planning my escape and checking details that I thought might be important.

Somewhere I got the idea of hiding in an Austria-bound train. So I spent a lot of time in railroad terminals watching the activities and learning time tables. I even made several trips from Praha to Brno just to see if there were some place where I might possibly hide. But there was no place anywhere inside.

Someone told me that during the war, partisans, or wanted people sometimes traveled under the locomotives in a small place above the axle. They said it was dangerous but that it could be done.

I decided it was worth the risk. From watching the trains and different terminals, I found that I would have to be hidden before the train got to Brno because at every stop past Brno, there were guards stationed around the trains which were leaving Czechoslovakia. But I was not sure whether or not the guards ever searched underneath the trains. I could not think of any way to find out since I could not possibly get close to the border. But it was imperative for me to know for certain.

Luckily that summer I met a tourist from Vienna, I swore him to secrecy of my plans and told him of my predicament. He promised to help me. But I needed to find some way for him to let me know how many times and at what points the guards inspected the trains. Most important of all, I needed to know whether they inspected underneath. It was impossible for him to write about such a thing through ordinary correspondence and the man did not plan to come back nor did he know of anyone who might relay the information to me.

I finally hit upon an idea I thought might work. I knew that when the man returned home, he would surely write to his host. In the letter he could send his regards to me and we could make an agreement of some coded way of letting me know about the border inspection. The plan seemed logical and the tourist agreed to mention my name in his host's letter.

As a signal to me, he would simply comment on the weather during his trip. Sunshine would be the good sign: there was no checking under the train. Any worsening in the weather would denote to what degree the train was inspected. Any other information would have to be disguised.

Within a few days after the tourist left, his host came to tell me that his friend had gotten home all right and that he sent his regards to me.

"May I read the letter?" I asked.

"Certainly. I brought it with me so you could read it."

It was just a picture postcard, but it contained the information I needed so badly.

"The weather was terrible all the way," the card read. "We traveled through a storm the entire way."

"That's too bad," I reflected aloud.

"What's too bad?"

"Oh, nothing," I realized I had said something inappropriate. "I was just thinking he could have seen some beautiful scenery on his trip, but he says that they had very bad weather."

"Ja, it is too bad," my informer's host agreed.

15. COMPANIONSHIP

I had always wanted to find a companion to go along with me when I tried to escape. A friend would make things much easier. I knew no one in Austria and I was uncertain of what kind of life to expect if I were successful. When I went to Brno shortly after graduation in June to take the entrance examination for college, I found such a person.

After the test was over, I stopped to make a short visit in church in thanksgiving for passing the test. I was surprised to find one of the boys, who had just taken the test with me, kneeling before the altar. As we left the church, we started a conversation that was to have a direct bearing on both our futures.

Pepek (my new acquaintance) told me of his struggle of attending school. His story was much the same as mine, except that he had been allowed to attend only the technical high school.

I commented that even though I had attended the gymnasium, I was also stuck with the mechanical college despite the fact that I had no special interest in mechanics.

"Mechanical college is decidedly not the place I would like to attend either. If I were free, I would be in a seminary," he confided.

The fact that I had met Pepek at church, and he had spoken of going to the seminary made me trust him immediately. Later I found that if I had met him under different circumstances, I would have probably felt the same about him; he was a very likeable young man. As our conversation continued, he again expressed his desire to be free.

"Have you ever thought of escaping?" I asked searchingly.

161

"Who hasn't? But what good does it do to only think about it?" Pepek lamented. "That's all we can do—just think."

"Maybe," I said absent-mindedly.

"If you have something up your sleeve, please tell me."

I assured him that I did not know of any possibility but was only making conversation. He was so sincere in his appeal, I immediately sensed that he was the boy I was looking for. Naturally I did not mention my plan to him at the time. I could always ask him to go along. First I had to find out more about him.

Because of my factory training, I was hired as a regular employee during the summer in the factory in which I had worked before I went to high school. As it happened, Pepek was also hired as a summer helper in the same factory, but we did not see each other too often at first.

I had to be positive of Pepek before I asked him to join me in my plans. I spent a lot of time during the summer making inquiries about him and found that Pepek was from a town near Hradsko. His family had owned a large factory that employed many workers. When his father saw that the communists were beginning to confiscate larger factories, he prudently started dividing his property and entrusting it to his most reliable employees with the understanding that they were to act as custodians. In that way, even after the communists seized the factory, the family still had a portion of their holdings to sustain them comfortably because the custodians proved trustworthy. I found that his family was highly respected, and Pepek himself seemed like a good risk, so I decided that if I ever had the chance to escape, I would ask Pepek to go, too.

Vacation time came and was almost over, but my plans to escape had not materialized. Try as I might, I could not find even the smallest "dent" in the Iron Curtain. In my efforts to learn all I could about the border, and the possibilities of escaping about the end of August, I met a man whom I felt confident I could trust. I shall call this man Bohuslav. But

162

because he is still very much alive and active beyond those barbed wires, I cannot give any other details about him, except to say that Bohuslav told me of another man who had recently returned to Czechoslovakia from Austria.

"This man was in Vienna only last spring," Bohuslav declared.

"How can that be?" I asked skeptically. "Are you sure?"

"As sure as I know I'm standing here. I don't know what kind of business he is in or how he managed to do it, but I do know that he was actually in Vienna and he is now back in Czechoslovakia," Bohuslav insisted. "If you'd like, I could arrange a meeting with him for you so you can see for yourself what you think. You could talk to him and then decide what you think your chances are of getting out of the country with him."

"That would be wonderful, Bohuslav! I would like to contact him as soon as possible."

Two days later Bohuslav came to tell me that he had arranged a meeting with his mysterious friend for the next afternoon at three o'clock in the railroad station in Zamky. His friend was to be standing at the third window from the left in the hall of the station wearing a montgomerak.

"You can't miss him," Bohuslav assured me. "Look for a man with a crooked nose."

"A crooked nose?"

"Yes, he is a boxer and about a year ago somebody broke his nose."

"O. K. Not many people have a crooked nose so he ought to be easy to spot. But how will he know who I am?"

"Just tell him that I sent you. That will be enough."

I could hardly believe my good fortune. I had tried so long without success to find even the remotest clue to someone like Bohuslav's friend. Then suddenly I not only knew of someone, but a meeting was already arranged.

My first impulse was to picture Bohuslav's friend as a man of great audacity and strength. I was impressed that he was

163

a boxer and visualized him as having a flawless physique. I imagined that he was the essence of composure and self-confidence. Upon further reflection, I wondered what his reasons could be for the type of work he did. I hoped that his reasons were of the noblest nature. I wanted to think that he had an ax to grind with the communists, and helping people escape was his way of retaliating for some wrong that had been heaped upon him. I was secretly ashamed that the thought that he might be a mercenary even crossed my mind. I fancied him as my savior and I immediately dismissed my suspicions. "Whatever his reasons are," I chided myself, "I will soon see. Why he takes such jobs, I don't know and I don't care. I only hope he can and will help me."

The next afternoon I went to Zamky to keep my appointment. As I approached the third window on the left of the station's hall, I saw no one to fit my mental description. The only man standing there was a young fellow who was only a little older than I, lazily puffing on a cigarette. The only distinctive thing about him was his crooked nose. "Surely he cannot be the one who defies all the dangers at the border," I thought in wonderment. I watched him for a moment before I approached him hesitantly and ventured, "My friend, Bohuslav, told me that I could find a friend of his here."

The man continued to vacantly watch the people as they passed. He took a long draw on his cigarette before he slowly turned to me and replied, "Yes, I am Bohuslav's friend. My name is Franta."

I introduced myself and offered my hand. He made a deliberate appraisal of me before he half-heartedly offered his.

If I expected him to start to ask questions, I was mistaken. I soon realized that it must be I who was to start the conversation, but I hardly knew where to begin.

"Shall we go to the restaurant?" I stammered.

"No, let's go to the park. We can talk there without having the walls around us."

164

"That's a good idea," I agreed.

We walked to the nearby park without further conversation, found a secluded bench, and sat down. Again it was I who had to start the conversation.

"I understand that you have some first-hand knowledge of the Iron Curtain."

I waited for an answer, but Franta seemed oblivious to me. His eyes were scrutinizing two passing women. It wasn't until they passed that he commented indifferently, "I was in Vienna for a few days last spring." His remark had about as much feeling as if he were saying that he had gone to a neighboring village.

My first impression of Franta was a disappointment. I had expected a daring man-of-the-world type and found instead a much younger person than I expected with a slim frame and a childish face. His eyes had a most unsettling, shifty look about them. His lips were set in a wry sort of smile. There was nothing about his physical appearance that made me like him instantly. But to a drowning man, even a match looks like like something to cling to. So I saw in Franta what I wanted to see.

"Perhaps this type of man is better than the one I visualized," I thought as I noted his desultory mannerisms. "No one would ever suspect that this fellow could do the things that are attributed to him. The fact that he looks shiftless may be to my advantage. If his plans become muddled, he can probably change them with no trouble, whereas a more tenacious type, who seems to be self-confident, may not have the flexibility to change his course when he encounters an obstacle in his plan."

His habit of not ever looking me directly in the eye unnerved me, but Franta was my only means of escape. I saw him as my rescuer and I decided to trust him implicitly. I had to. There was no alternative.

"Why did you come back once you were free?" I inquired.

"I had to. My mother is here and she depends entirely on

165

me for her support." He paused to let a group of young men go by, then added, "My older brother escaped in 1949."

"That does make a difference," I commented trying to understand his situation, but my curiosity was not satisfied. "What did you do in Vienna?"

He looked at me fleetingly and then smiled slyly. His eyes shifted from place to place before setting on a group of workers who were rushing to catch the train. Finally he said almost in a whisper. "Oh, I just went there to buy some chocolate and chewing gum, that's all." His eyes darted back to me and he smiled again.

Obviously he felt it was none of my business as to why he risked his life two different times crossing the border to and from Austria. I felt a little ridiculous at having asked such a question.

"I'm sorry I asked. I should have known better," I apologized.

"That's all right," he said without the least show of irritation.

I decided to come straight to the point.

"Would you help me cross the border?"

"I don't have a reason for going just now. But the situation could change in one hour," he said mysteriously.

"If you aren't going yourself, could you tell me if there is any way I can make it alone? I'll appreciate any kind of information I can get. I'm not especially asking you to take me with you if you don't plan to go, but I need all the information I can get. I am willing to pay."

"We can talk about money later. Just be ready to go any time from now. I never know what will come up."

"O. K. I'll be ready," I said with great enthusiasm. "But you don't know my address."

"Yes, I do. Bohuslav told me about you. In case something turns up, I will contact you through Bohuslav. Within the week, I am supposed to find out how soon I will have to go again. If I don't contact you before then, meet me here at this same bench at the same time next Wednesday."

I felt satisfied at the meeting with Franta. He seemed so casual about crossing the Iron Curtain, as thought it were no trick at all. I was especially pleased that he was not insistent on money. I felt it was a good sign. I had heard of those who were in such risky business only for the money. They didn't really care about the people once they were paid. Often they collected their fee and left the escapees on their own. Or worse, they sometimes even made deals with the communists or the guards to turn them in so that they could collect a reward or get other privileges. What was more important to them, they didn't have to risk their own necks. Franta had not even mentioned money so I thought the outlook was most promising.

After I decided to trust Franta, I decided to see if Pepek wanted to go along. The next day after my meeting with Franta, I found Pepek alone so I barely hinted at the idea of escaping. He eagerly jumped at my bait.

"Please tell me truthfully, Peter, if you were only making conversation the first time we met or do you have a plan?"

"Don't ask such questions if you are not sure you want to follow them up," I advised.

"That's the point. I want to escape, but I don't know how. If you have a plan, please let me go with you."

"All right, Pepek, I'll tell you. I am making plans with someone who has already made the crossing both ways. I do not know how he did it, or where, or anything else. But he has promised to take me with him the next time he goes."

"Will you ask him to take me, too?"

"I will if you are sure you want to go. Do you understand the dangers?"

"I understand all right. But I know I can't stay here forever. Count me in on your plans," Pepek urged excitedly.

It was settled. Pepek and I would go as a team. I felt better knowing someone would be going with me.

Pepek went with me when I met Franta the next Wednes-

167

day. Franta agreed to have Pepek go with us.

"I can't promise you anything definite, but it could be at any time. Stay at home in case I have to contact you immediately," Franta instructed us. "You can rest assured that we will go sometime within three months." After a long hesitation he said, "One more thing, a venture like this takes money."

"How much?" I asked.

"Understand it doesn't depend completely on me."

"I understand, but could you tell us approximately?"

"Well, keep something like 4,000 korun on hand just in case," he advised.

Four thousand korun was a staggering amount for me. In my financial condition, it was more than I could hope to save in so short a time. Privately Pepek assured me that he could raise the rest of whatever money was needed so we made a deal with Franta: 4,000 korun for leading us out of Czechoslovakia.

During the next month, Franta came to see me. When I saw him, a great surge of excitement filled me. I thought he was coming to tell me that he was ready to go. But instead he came for some money.

"This 'business' I'm in costs a lot of money," was his explanation.

"How much do you need?" I inquired.

"Just an advance. Something has come up that I need to take care of, 1,500 korun ought to do. You can give me the rest of the 4,000 later."

Fifteen hundred korun was almost everything I had saved since I first gotten the idea to try to find someone to help me. It had not been easy to save that much, but I gave it to Franta in the hope that it was the best spent money of my life.

16. INTERIM

According to Franta's original time-table, we were to leave about the end of October. Since both Pepek and I had already enrolled in college, we decided the wisest course was to go ahead with our plans despite the fact that we didn't plan to stay in college but a few weeks at most. We lived in the same dormitory so Franta could contact us at a moment's notice.

School started and we witnessed a completely new kind of life, college students' life. The curriculum emphasized math, physics, mechanical drawing, Russian, and especially Marx-Leninism.

I did not study as I ordinarily would have. I did just what I had to and nothing more. My mind concentrated on Franta's call, but I enjoyed some of the classes anyway. The most interesting (and ambiguous) classes were in Marx-Leninism.

We not only had the assembly lectures in communistic doctrine, at which about five hundred students attended, we also had semi-weekly discussion sessions.

During the assembly lectures, a teacher, who looked more like a dunce than a college professor and who always wore the communist's insignia on his coat, expounded on Marx-Lenin's theories. His lectures were insipid and boring, but he never seemed to tire of reiterating his statements even though the students never listened. Some of them read the sports page of newspapers; others played tick-tack-toe; but most of them slept. Only those sitting close to the rostrum paid any attention.

One lecture that I particularly remember was when he was impugning the philosophy of St. Thomas Aquinas, the founder of the philosophical school of thought in the thirteenth century which rejuvenated man's thinking on his own worth.

169

The teacher exclaimed, "Isn't it ridiculous for educated men, such as the philosophers who adhere to Thomas Aquinas' logic, to sit for hours and to discuss such nonsense as whether an angel can dance on the point of a needle?"

If the teacher expected the students to laugh, he was mistaken. Instead, one of the students who paid attention heckled, "What do you think, Comrade, can he?"

The teacher was at a complete loss for words. He didn't know what to say. His mouth began to move but no words came out.

Only then did the students laugh. First, those who paid attention began to laugh. Those who were not listening looked up and asked what was going on. Their laughter in turn roused the sleeping students. As each group set off a chain reaction, it sounded like waves of laughter engulfing the hall. It took a long time before the teacher could continue his lecture.

I was surprised at the atmosphere of those classes. All the students had been closely screened before they had been accepted in the college. I felt sure that there could not have been too many like Pepek and me, who were diametrically opposed to the communist's teachings, that had been overlooked during the entrance screenings, but still there was a definite undercurrent of discontent even among those who were favorable to communism. It was more pronounced in the discussion sessions.

Each discussion class consisted of only fifteen to twenty students. The book for those classes was Karl Marx's *Kapital,* and the teacher, who was a young doctor of philosophy, gave plenty of time for open discussion. It was amazing to what lengths the discussions went.

Once the doctor spoke about Marx's theory of a classless society. He maintained that we were very close to achieving that end at that time.

One of the students raised his hand and said outright that it was not true.

170

"What do you mean, 'it's not true'?" the doctor asked. "Can you show me any capitalists in Czechoslovakia?"

"No, we don't have any capitalists," the student had to admit. "At least not the capitalists who are owners of factories. But we do most certainly have class distinction. Look at the president of the factories and the high officials of the Party. It is true that they don't own the factories, but they have big salaries while we slave and hardly earn more than our substance; they have privileges the working man does not have, like going on foreign vacations or skiing in the mountains in the winter as part of their 'recreation,' while we are 'allowed' to work in the *brigadas* for ours; they live in nice villas; the ordinary worker lives in substandard housing with no conveniences; they have big cars at their disposal while we ride bicycles or ride in dirty trains where there is not enough room to sit down after a hard day's work."

When the doctor tried to curtail the discussion and say that it was not as bad as the student claimed, a girl interrupted, "Yes, it is, Comrade. Last month, just before I came here, I was working in a factory. One day after work a boy tripped and was almost trampled to death as he tried to get on a bus near the factory at the end of the daylight shift just because the workers were so determined to get on that bus. If they missed that one, they would have had to wait two hours for the next one. The busses are so crowded that the workers are jammed together like sardines. You have to ride standing on one leg and that leg is not your own."

"And what about the poor people?" argued another boy. "There are not supposed to be any beggars in the communistic society because there are no employers to exploit the poor. But go down town and see how many beggars you see. Just the other day I was eating in a restaurant and an old lady came begging for a piece of bread. She told me that she gets only 120 korun a month. After she pays her rent, she does not have enough to live on."

Another time there was a big discussion about the relationship between Czech students and those from other countries. Foreign students were a constant and severe source of agitation among the students.

"How is it that they live in new, modern buildings, with only two or three to a room while twenty or twenty-five of us are crammed into dormitories. We do not have enough room to do our mechanical drawing assignments or hang our clothes; we have no laundry facilities or showers; but still we must pay while everything is free to them. The Africans, Vietnamese, Bulgarians, and others get sizable scholarships and have elegant clothes and cameras. They go to the coast during vacation while we are forced to work really hard in the *brigadas* just for a chance to continue our studies. We count every korun, while they always have money. They get by with easier exams because they claim they do not understand the language. But in spite of all this, we are asked to be gracious to the foreigners and to show them our 'love' while they are ridiculing us behind our backs."

I thought it was very dangerous for the students to talk so openly, and I never joined in this type of discussion. Usually they expressed their opinions in question form as: "Is it not true, Comrade, etc?" rather than by arguing. But a very definite dissatisfaction existed and the students often showed it openly.

Then in November, 1956, something happened which caused me to leave college.

The anti-communists in Hungary started a revolution. Our two countries had such political ties that, whatever the outcome of Hungary's revolt, it would naturally affect us.

During the first few days of the revolt, all conversations were centered on what was happening in Hungary. We had no radios in our dormitories, but some of the boys went to private homes near the campus to listen to the Voice of America and Radio Free Europe. They brought back the latest news. In the beginning, we all thought that the communists would squash the revolt within a few hours or within

172

a few days at the most because the communists not only had the army and police on their side, but the Russian Army's occupational forces as well, while the patriots were virtually unarmed. But the Hungarian people had an invincible will to win, and they turned the tide of the revolt with their bare hands, as it were. The communists were actually losing their grip.

Whispers began to circulate about a manifestation that was planned in Brno in support of the Hungarian people. We received word that all students from the colleges and the University in Brno would march through the town in a display of solidarity for the freedom fighters. The day, time, and place of the parade was set. But in the last few hours before the parade, the S. T. B. stepped in and infiltrated the whole plan. It was impossible to reorganize anything when secret police were everywhere. Soon the police began to look for those who had organized the idea of the march, and I realized it was time for me to leave college. Although I had not taken part in organizing the march, I was afraid that the very fact of my presence there at the time of such insubordination might make me liable. As the authorities went through the *cadre cards,* mine would surely turn up and indicate my negative position.

The reason I gave in the office for quitting was that I was financially unable to continue. I told the registrar that I had hoped to receive a scholarship. Since I had not, I could not afford to stay. What I didn't say was that I had given Franta the last of my savings, and I was compelled to quit school and go to work to earn my share of the money that we had promised Franta.

I did not risk anything leaving college when I did. The year's draft quota was called at the end of each October or the beginning of each November. Those who were called that year were already gone so I had a whole year before I had to worry about being drafted into the army.

For a very short time, it looked as though I might not

173

need to escape after all. The revolt in Hungary was going so well in favor of the freedom fighters that the flames of revolt were being fanned everywhere. Limited fighting had even started in the eastern part of Slovakia.

Emotions were running very strongly. The people fully expected something wonderful to happen. It was evident that the Party members were becoming nervous. Their entire attitude changed. Some of them acted as though they had been forced to join the Party because of their jobs. Others openly said that they did not want to harm anyone; they had only followed orders. But not everyone could find an excuse for joining or being active, and they clearly worried about what would happen to them if a revolution broke out in Czechoslovakia.

The *Kadrovy* of the factory in which I worked was alleged to have said that he had a machine gun at home and would use every bullet to defend himself, except the last one which he would save for himself.

Some of the men were called to the army. It was not a general mobilization. Army officers personally went to the men's homes and factories to deliver the orders. I saw some of the draftees in Zamky marching through the town still wearing civilian clothes. I knew many of them personally. Only one among those whom I knew was a devoted communist. The rest were anything but sympathetic to the Party; two of them had brothers in concentration camps. If these men were called upon to fight, it was inconceivable to me that they would have fought the unarmed civilians in defence of the dictatorship that was exploiting them and their families.

We, as well as the Hungarians, waited in vain for help from the Western powers. Their intervention would have been the green light for further uprisings. It was the sole encouragement we needed. But unfortunately, help did not come.

When Khrushchev saw that help was not coming to the Hungarians, he ordered the Red Army to take Hungary by force. It was futile for the Hungarian heroes to fight the regular

174

army of the Soviet Union. And the revolt was crushed.

The communists in Czechoslovakia promptly regained their self-assurance. The Party members were secure in their positions once more, and more contemptuous (it seemed to me) than before.

I was at home without a job and realized that the political climate would not change for the better. I knew I must continue to plan my escape. I began to look for a job to make money to pay Franta. I was lucky to find one very soon. I was hired as an instructor in the *internat* where I had been an apprentice.

The top communists in the factory didn't like the idea of my working with the youths, but because they could not find any other qualified man, I was accepted with the stipulation: "For trial only." As long as I did not have a "bad influence" on the young people, and they could not find a replacement, I had a job.

I liked to work with the fifteen and sixteen year-old apprentices. I could not do very much for them because I was constantly under the watchful eyes of the new director, Comrade Holub, who had replaced Comrade Desatnik. Comrade Holub was not only a dedicated member of the Party, he was also a member of the S. T. B. so I had to be exceedingly careful.

My duties at the *internat* were to instruct the apprentices on how to operate different machines in the factory; therefore, I had nothing to do with politics or ideologies.

The salary was about average for that type of work. I got 900 korun a month after taxes. I soon realized I had made a good decision when I left school to go to work. Franta came again and asked for more money. Pepek would have paid more than his share if I could not have raised the money, but I wanted to pay my part, if at all possible.

Several times we met with Franta, but each time he had a different reason why we could not go, so we tried to be patient. When Pepek showed his irritation at Franta's long delays, Franta returned, "I really don't know when we will go. Everything is uncertain now because of the revolution."

"Do you think you will go soon?" I asked impatiently. We were growing more nervous by the day.

"I'm sure we'll go soon, but you will have to be patient a little longer," Franta advised.

So we tried to be patient. Christmas came and went, then New Years, and February, but still Franta didn't call us. Each time was saw him, he had a different reason.

After the revolution, his excuse was that the guards on the border were more cautious than ever. Then it was the snow that stopped us (our tracks could have been followed too easily). After the snow melted, Franta still claimed he was waiting for important news. Each of his excuses was credible, so we waited.

Again Franta needed money. He said he could not take us for the original 4,000 korun we had agreed upon. He would need 8,000.

When I told Pepek, he decided to leave college, too, and go to work. He did not want to ask his parents for that large a sum. He would have to give them some reason why he needed it, but he did not want to involve them in our scheme. The only job he could find was in the mines in Ostrava. The work was really hard, but he was able to make some money.

The spring of 1957 found Pepek and me working, skimping and saving, with Franta always asking for more.

17. FOOLHARDINESS

My foolhardy actions against the communists during the elections of 1957 almost ruined my life.

It was the second election in which I was old enough to vote. The first time I voted was in 1955 and that election was anything but "free" because the candidates were hand picked by the communists, not on the basis of who would best represent the people, but on who would best serve the Party. There was no such thing as a write-in candidate either. But in the 1957 elections, the election judges were merely local people who did not especially lean toward the communists. There was at least a little simulation of a fair election because the people were not meticulously watched, and they felt a little "free" to exert their contempt. The local communists considered the people's actions a near disaster for the Party, and were afraid to report to their superiors that so many of the ballots were destroyed or mutilated. Their report of the votes counted showed that 97% were in favor of the communists' candidates.

But if the previous elections had been considered a farce, then (from what I witnessed) the elections of 1957 were a mockery of the democratic process.

In the election, the candidates were again selected well in advance by the Communist Party, and their choice was made public in a meeting several weeks before the election. The people of our district were most dissatisfied with the Party's choice for our representative, and asked to have him replaced. The chairman of the meeting, who was an ardent communist, said it could not be done.

"So what is the election for if we can't vote for the one we want to be our representative?" argued the most aggressive

177

man. The chairman promised that the Party would review their choice and hold another meeting the next week.

Meantime the *Kadrovy* of the factory where the man worked called the man who had stood up and publicly criticized the candidate into his office and warned him, "We want this candidate elected. You keep your mouth shut. If you don't, we may find it necessary to send some of our workers to the mines. Do I make myself clear?"

The man understood the *Kadrovy's* insinuated threat all too well.

The next week, arriving in a car, the chairman of the meeting brought three more men whom we did not know, but they wore the communist's insignia on their coats, so we assumed they were communists (it was a logical assumption —no one but communists wore the insignia or rode in cars).

The meeting was very subdued. No one had the courage to speak out against the candidate. The man who had been so outspoken before didn't say a single word. It would have been useless anyway because the choice of all the candidates had been settled beforehand, and the Party refused to replace the unpopular candidate.

Outside the meeting, there was much discussion as to how to go about voting against the candidates. The people did not know, nor could they find out. Some of them said the best way to vote against a candidate was to destroy the ballot so that it couldn't be counted. (The ballots consisted of an envelope and a small piece of paper for each office with a single candidate's name printed on each slip.) Others maintained that it was better to drop an empty envelope into the ballot box; the most popular opinion was to scratch out the candidate's name. But no one knew for sure if any of these ways would be counted as a vote *against* the candidate—they had not been in previous elections. It was common knowledge that however the people voted, the election's result was determined before a single ballot was cast.

I knew that whichever way I voted, I would not change

anything, but for me a matter of principle was involved. I felt that we had an inherent right to a free vote, and I was determined to assert that right. I decided that, come what may, I would go into the booth and scratch all the candidate's names with a double line.

The elections were held on a Sunday in May. I went to vote at 1:30 p.m. On the way to the school building, which was the appointed voting place for our precinct, I met two of my boyhood chums. They told me that they would like to vote against the candidates, but they knew it was useless because the outcome of the election was already settled.

"I've heard that the judges put a notation by the names of everyone who goes behind the curtain," cautioned one of the boys.

"I've heard that, too. So whether I will go into the voting booth depends on who the election judges are," said the other boy.

I was well aware that the judges were watching every voter. If a voter simply placed all the ballots into the envelope and dropped it into the ballot box in full view, they knew that he had voted for their candidates. To go behind the curtain of the booth was to admit that the voter was trying to vote against them. The penalty for voting "against the working class" could be expulsion from the job or school, or being sent to the mines or to the army. The least they would do was to make a notation of the voter's action on his *cadre card*.

As we approached the school, we met several people who had just fulfilled their *abcanskou povinnost* (citizen's obligation), and they did not seem very happy about it. One of them told us that two men from my factory were appointed as election judges.

"What rotten luck," I thought. "That means that they will know me and they will especially be watching me."

But I had promised myself that I would perform this one last act of defiance before I left my country. If I were going to be accused of the "crime" of trying to escape, I may as

179

well also commit the "crime" of voting against the regime.

As we entered our classroom, I noticed that all the desks had been removed from the room, leaving it without furniture except for two long tables, a small table that held the ballot box, and the voting booth. The judges' long tables were directly opposite the door and set to form an "L." To the left only a few feet from the end of the long tables was the ballot box. (I felt sure it was placed near the end of the table to make it easy for the judges to watch the voters get their ballots, put them into envelopes, drop them into the box, and leave.) Aside in the corner behind the judges' table was the voting booth. It was a small, awkward, curtained stall, placed in such a position that voters who insisted on using it would become conspicuous. It was a standing joke even among the communists. Even they laughed that it was so small that one needed a telescope to see it, nevertheless, it was strict rule of theirs to have it. Actually its only purpose was to try to deceive the Western reporters into believing that we had "free" elections. I had used the booth in the previous election. It was so small one could hardly get inside, with no place to set the ballot and no pencil to mark the ballot if one wanted to.

The first thing to catch my eye as I entered the room was the judges seated behind the table. Two of them were just local people who were not "with" the communists, but not particularly against them either. The two other judges were what dismayed me. Seated in the two chairs closest to the ballot box was the president of the Communist Party from my factory and my immediate superior, Comrade Holub, who was director of the *internat*. Neither of them lived in Hradsko, but they were professional communists who went about the whole district trying to influence the people; consequently, it was natural for them to act as judges in our "free" election.

It was no secret that neither of them liked me nor the fact that I was an instructor in the *internat*. The president of the Communist Party made it exceedingly plain to me when he hired me, saying, "You can stay here only so long as you

180

prove to us that going to school has changed you."

I entered the room, trying to look very casual even though inwardly I was tied in knots.

"Dobry den" (Good day), I said to everyone in general. Except for one of the teachers who was checking the ballots for my friends who had gone before me, everyone looked up.

"Dobry den," replied the city clerk and the one teacher.

Comrade Holub made no reply at all.

"Cest praci," retorted the president of the Party from our factory in a most rebuking tone. "I'm surprised at you."

I knew that the president's caustic reply was a rebuke for using the "bourgeois" greeting, so I busied myself with the teacher who was handing out ballots.

Lying on the table in front of Comrade Holub was the book in which all the names and other information about each voter were listed. "So it will be he who will make the notation in front of my name when I go into the booth," I thought. To him I said as gaily as I could muster, "You know my name, don't you?"

He checked to find my name without any comment or without even looking at me.

I noticed that my friends had put their ballots into their envelopes and dropped them into the ballot box and were already leaving.

As I started to walk between the table and the ballot box to go into the voting booth. Comrade President motioned with his finger and said icily, "Comrade Esterka, the ballot box is there."

"I know," I replied, "but I would like to use the voting booth."

He looked at me unbelievingly and turned so abruptly that even the chair he was sitting on turned with him.

"You can't do that," he exclaimed emphatically.

"Why not? I understand that this is a secret election."

When I said that, everyone turned to stare at me in disbelief at what they had heard.

181

"You know, Comrade Esterka, that you are supposed to vote openly," be retorted sternly as he arose from his chair and started to walk toward me.

"But I would like to use the booth," I shrugged.

"You are supposed to vote openly!" he kept repeating.

"If I can't use the voting booth, why is it there?" I tried to act very dense.

"You must not go behind the curtain," he yelled. "We let you teach our youths. You *must* vote openly!"

I didn't see a connection between teaching youths how to operate machinery and voting openly, but I said, trying to appear calm, "O. K., O. K. if you think I must vote openly, I will."

I went to the ballot box, set the ballots on top of it, and ostentatiously reached into my pocket for my pencil, and began to scratch the names on each ballot very deliberately. "O. K., first, second. . . . and here we have the last one that I don't want to represent me anywhere," I proclaimed.

I put the ballots into the envelope and tossed them into the ballot box. "Are you *satisfied now?*" I asked challengingly.

The same evening of the election, I learned from one of the teachers who was an election judge that, as soon as I left, the president and Comrade Holub decided to fire me.

Because it was just at test time in the *internat,* and they could not find a qualified replacement, I was not fired immediately, but I knew it was only a question of time.

For several days after the election everything seemed normal. Comrade Holub never mentioned their decision of firing me, and I, too, tried to act as though nothing had happened.

Naturally, the communists' candidates won the election— they had to, they had no opponents. They claimed that they won with a majority of over 95% of the people voting for their candidates.

A few days later something drastic happened.

Just before the daylight shift was over, the *Kadrovy* came

to me personally and told me to report to the S. T. B. Headquarters immediately.

"They want to talk with you," was the only explanation he would give me.

The S. T. B. in Czechoslovakia is the equivalent of the dreaded N. K. V. D. in Russia or the infamous Nazi Gestapo, and to fall into their hands was the worst possible thing that could happen. If they wanted information or a "confession," they had very effective methods of obtaining it even if the accused had heard about the "crime" for the first time from them.

Instinctively I began to examine my conscience as to the reason they had called me. "Did I say something against the regime or some influential member of the Party? No, I can't recall anything and I'm sure I would remember if I did because I have been especially careful lately. Well, did I do something against them? The election! Yea, that's it. It must be. But it is too soon for them to take any reprisals against me for what I did at the elections. Calling me in so soon after the elections would cause many people to talk about it too much. They may do something about it later perhaps, but now is too soon." I racked my brain for any other reason, but couldn't think of anything I had done.

"The escape! Perhaps they know or suspect something about our plan," I gasped in horror. "But that is impossible. If they suspected something like that, they wouldn't send for me; they would have already come for me."

It was a terrible feeling to know that I may be arrested and perhaps imprisoned for something I couldn't even remember doing. As I walked hesitantly to the S. T. B. Headquarters, I began to panic. "I know what I'll do," I said almost aloud, "I'll disappear and hide somewhere, and somehow get in contact with Franta to let him know that my situation is desperate and that it is absolutely imperative that we make a break for it now."

Only a moment's reflection made me realize that the scheme

183

would never work. There were too many problems: if they wanted me badly enough, someone was probably watching me at that very instant; even if I could elude them (which almost certainly I could not), there were the problems of where to hide and how to get in touch with Pepek or Franta.

I was frantic.

Along the way I met a girl I knew from school. "Please, Milena, would you do me a favor?" I begged.

"Sure. What?"

"I've been summoned by the S.T.B. That's where I'm going now. You are the only one who knows about it. In case I'm not home by tomorrow morning, please tell my parents where I am. I know they will worry about me."

"All right. I'll tell them," she promised. "Do you know what they want you for?"

"That's just the trouble. I don't have the vaguest idea. I'm afraid to talk to you any more; someone may be watching. But, please, tell my parents."

And I walked on to my inevitable fate.

The S. T. B. Headquarters was about a forty-five minute walk from the factory. I delayed getting there as long as I dared. If someone were following me, it was wisest to go there directly. I arrived at the headquarters which were housed in a beautiful villa that had been confiscated from a man who was formerly Zamky's richest business man but who was then an "enemy of the working people."

I gave my name to a uniformed guard at the entrance. Without a word, he pressed a button that electrically opened the door. I stepped inside into a large foyer. I became more forlorn with each passing minute.

After a little while, another uniformed policeman came and beckoned me to follow him. I obeyed even though my mind was spinning with a thousand questions. We walked down a long corridor that was lined with several doors each bearing a number. The corridor made a right angle and only a few feet further, we came to a wall of bars. The policeman rang

184

a signal bell that was promptly answered by a guard who asked my name. Upon hearing it, he unlocked the door in the wall of bars and only I stepped through.

The clang of the door as it rattled closed was the most desolate sound I've ever heard.

"My God, I'm trapped."

After telling me to wait, the guard who unlocked the door disappeared behind the door from which he came.

I looked around at my surroundings, the deserted hall, more numbered doors, several barred windows that gave a view of a lovely garden with a high, formidable, brick wall beyond it.

"There is no way out of here. Even the lovely garden is surrounded by a bleak wall." I recoiled.

Again my thoughts turned to my own plight. "Why am I here? What have I done? Oh, if only I knew!"

The dreadful stories I had heard about others who had been brought before the S. T. B. boomed before me like eerie illusions. There was the boy I knew who had been accused of being an "enemy of the working class" for burning up a huge hay stack that belonged to a commune. He was arrested and jailed. The next night another hay stack was burned. The boy was forced to sign a confession saying that he had set both fires although it was impossible for him to have set the second fire since he was in jail at the time. But the communists had their confession and their scapegoat. Recalling other such morbid tales made me a little sick.

There was no place to sit down. It was getting late and I was tired and hungry. My mind was reeling from asking myself over and over a thousand times, "What have I done? Why am I here? What do they want?" I've never before or since known such mental anguish. Time stretched on endlessly. I listened attentively for a sound—any sound—but everything was deadly silent. Every nerve in my body quivered. For two interminably long hours I waited and prayed . . .

About 4 o'clock a man in civilian clothes called me into

one of the offices. He motioned me to have a chair in front of the desk.

The man was middle aged and rather nice looking. I was soon to find that he had a disarming way about him. I watched his expression, trying to anticipate what the mood of the interview would be, but he was completely expressionless.

He sat down behind the desk and slowly pulled out a drawer from which he brought out a massive filing folder. He set it on the desk and began deliberately to thumb through it. My eyes were riveted on the file as I realized that it was my *cadre card*. It had information about me in it that I had completely forgotten—every argument and remark I had made to Comrade Stika and Comrade Desatnik long ago; remarks I had made in the factory and high school; places I had been; people I had talked to. The communists certainly had effective informers. I sensed an uneasy feeling that the man behind the desk knew me better than I knew myself.

The first questions he asked were of a general nature and I began to relax a little. From these first innocent questions he came to more important things. Again I had to explain why I wouldn't join the C. S. M. or the Communist Party. Slowly and delicately he steered the questions to my faith in God and my impression of morality. We talked at length about my views.

Finally, he asked, "Don't you realize that you can compromise your beliefs and live a comfortable life as a Party member?"

"I don't expect to live forever, sir. And when I die, I don't expect God will compromise his justice to suit me," I explained.

He looked at me rather thoughtfully as he mumbled something under his breath that I could not understand. He turned away from me and gazed out of the barred window for a long time before he turned again, and asked, "Would you like to be a priest?"

"I really don't know. I haven't had a chance to decide."

186

"Then why were you in the Bishop's Gymnasium?"

"I suppose at that time there was a possibility that I could have become a priest, but that was a long time ago."

"Wasn't that your intention when you went there?"

"I was only thirteen at that time. I'm sure I couldn't make any final decisions at that age."

"What would you do if you would have the chance to decide to be a priest today?"

"I don't know," was my honest reply.

"Do you think you would decide to be a priest?"

"I truly don't know. There would be many obstacles now. For one thing, I haven't studied Latin. But there are other problems, too."

"For example."

"Our only seminary is controlled by the government."

"So you think the seminary is no longer any good, is that it?"

"I didn't say that. I honestly don't know," I avowed.

The man seemed to have mellowed considerably from the beginning of our talk, and the interrogation turned to an unrestrained conversation that lasted a very long time. We spoke of many topics and ideas. I answered all his questions as honestly as I could. Whether it was his scheming way of worming information from me, I don't know. If it was, it was effective. I think I would have sincerely liked the man under normal conditions.

After about an hour and a half of such talk, another man entered while the first man whose name I never learned left.

I soon found that the second man was the exact opposite of the first. As well-disposed as the first man had been, that's how obnoxious the second man proved to be. Physically he was of average height and build, with nothing outstanding except that he had a defective eye, (one eye pulled outward) making him cockeyed. It was most disconcerting to look at him because I was never quite sure where he was looking.

He began to bagder me in harsh, loud tones and I again

became tense and on guard, being exceedingly careful with my answers. He interrogated me about every thing that I had ever done, not just in a direct way either. I needed to be very careful how I answered because he would slyly rephrase the question, trying to trick me. Every discussion Comrade Desatnik and I had had in the *internat* was rehashed. My "trial" by the company president and his commission, and every other phase of my life in the factory, high school, college was re-examined. He brought up things which were so inconsequential that I could not even remember they ever happened.

He was a detestable, villainous creature. I was getting so tired and hungry. Many times he became violent and he shouted obscenities at me, and I disliked him more with each question.

Questions. Pointless questions. Endless questions.

But I knew I could not let my guard down for an instant. To so many of the questions, I had to give answers with mental reservations.

"Do you listen to the Western radio programs?" he demanded.

That was a stupid question. Most people behind the Iron Curtain do (maybe he did, too), but I couldn't admit that I did, nor would anyone else.

"I don't have time to listen to the radio. I'm more interested in sports. Anyway, whenever I do listen, I don't want to hear a lot of talking. I like to listen to the music on Brno and Praha stations."

"I understand that you were at the movies last Saturday," he started a different line of questioning.

"Yes, that is true."

"Did you enjoy it?"

"Yes, very much."

"Even if it was a Russian movie?"

"If the movie was good, what do I care whether it's Russian, or Czech, or Polish?" I couldn't imagine where the line of questioning was being directed.

188

"Did you see the newsreel, too?"

"Yes."

"What do you think about the portable American helicopter?"

I was beginning to get the drift of his inquiry. The newsreel showed an American inventor and his portable helicopter that would be a real boon in escaping.

"I think it is a brilliant invention," I admitted.

"What would you do if you would have such a helicopter?" he taunted.

"That's a ridiculous question," I snorted, exasperatedly.

"In the first place, I can't get one; and if I could, I wouldn't have the money to buy one; but if I did have the money, I wouldn't know how to operate it or have any place to go in it."

Then he changed the subject completely.

"Do you think the Americans will come to—how do the people phrase it—to 'free' Czechoslovakia from us communists?" he asked sarcastically.

"No, I don't."

"Do you believe that they have already sent their spies into our country?"

"That's absurd!"

"Is it? Well, what would you do if an American spy came and asked you for help?"

"I don't believe there are any American spies here," I scoffed. "And if there were, they would not come to me for help."

"Don't get smart with me. Answer the question."

"I told you I don't know any spies."

I was getting tired and irritable and I found myself snapping back at him.

"But suppose one did contact you, what would you do? Would you help him?" he yelled.

"How could *I* help him?" I yelled back, trying to seem too dense to understand fully what he was asking.

189

He dwelled on the subject for a long time. I could not convince him with my elusive answers, so finally I said jeeringly, "I don't think any secret agent would contact me now since I am involved with the S. T. B."

My answer must have been the height of impertinence to the man. He literally jumped at me with clinched fists ready to strike, but the door opened at that moment and the man who had first talked to me entered.

A rebuking look passed from the first to the second man. The belligerent man dropped his fists, turned away, and walked to the window. Not a word was spoken between the two.

The first man handed me a piece of paper and asked me to sign it.

"May I read it first?" I asked.

He nodded as he walked to the desk and began to rearrange the papers of my cadre card.

I read the statement in which I promised not to disclose what we had talked about and that I had not been mistreated in any way. I signed without comment.

"Am I to keep quiet even about being here?" I asked.

The man advised that it would be better not to even reveal that I had been interrogated.

I was then led to the outer door and released. Imagine how I felt! A great emotion overwhelmed me. I was not being sent to a prison or concentration camp after all.

On the way to the bus station, I noticed that I was being followed. To be sure that it was not just a feeling, I stopped and looked into the store windows several times. My "shadow" always paused behind me.

I got off the bus in Hradsko and made sure I was no longer being followed before I went to the home of the girl whom I had asked to explain my where abouts to my parents.

"Please, don't tell anyone that I was even there," I begged. "It is better for me and you, too."

She tried to question me about what went on but I refused

to tell her. "Just forget the whole thing, will you. I told you it is better for us both."

From that day, my life became even more miserable than before. I knew that one small action, misconstrued by my watchdog as being a "crime against the regime" would send me to jail. I no longer stoked only little fires, I had a whole furnace blazing away.

I knew I had to be very careful. I eliminated all meetings with Franta. From then on, only Pepek saw Franta, and we agreed that Pepek would not come to me unless it was important.

I begged Pepek to tell Franta that I no longer had a choice of whether to go or not. For me, every day, hour, and minute brought me closer to my doom.

But Franta sent back only a demand for more money.

"Tell him that I can't wait any longer," I told Pepek. "They are watching every move I make and I won't wait any longer."

"Hold on a little longer, Peta," Pepek tried to reassure me. "Realize that it is not easy to risk your life for somebody else."

"Tell Franta that I will be satisfied with whatever information he can give me. He can keep the money, but I'm going—alone if I have to—but I'm going before the situation gets any worse. You can wait if you want, Pepek, but I'm not."

Pepek relayed my message to Franta. After a long hesitation (according to Pepek's later account), Franta agreed that he could take us the following Sunday.

"Have everything ready to go," Franta advised Pepek. "And be sure you have the rest of the 8,000 korun with you. I may need it."

The following Sunday Pepek and I waited and waited at our appointed rendezvous. But Franta did not come.

18. BETRAYED

Realizing that Franta was not coming, Pepek and I became suspicious. His reasons no longer seemed credible and we were tired of his excuses. We had to know what was going on.

We decided the best way to find out more about Franta was to go to Pisek, the town where he lived and see what we could find. Of course, we realized that we would need to be very discreet in our investigation of him. A stranger asking questions about Franta could possibly make the authorities suspicious of him, and if he were really our friend, it might jeopardize us as well as him.

Pepek had to return to work in the mines in Ostrava so he could not go to Pisek. I was on evening duty at the *internat* that week and had the mornings and early afternoons free. Pepek offered to leave his motorcycle with me that week so I could use it to go Pisek to check on Franta.

Our plan was devious, we knew, but we were desperate. We had to know more about Franta. The question was: who would give us the answers we needed? Obviously no one could tell us more about Franta than his own mother. If I was very careful, she might tell us all we needed to know without realizing it. We based our plan on the fact that when Bohuslav had first told me of Franta, he mentioned that long ago Franta's family and he had been neighbors for many years. Then old friendship was the key we needed.

It was early morning on Thursday when I arrived at the home of Franta's mother. It was located on a quiet street near an old Franciscan church. The house itself was small and old but neatly kept. A rose bush was blooming profusely

192

near the door. As I stood there, I couldn't help but feel extremely guilty about what I was doing. The whole plan was repulsive, but I had to go through with it.

An ordinary looking woman of about fifty answered my knock and acknowledged that she was Mrs. Franta. She welcomed me in when I introduced myself as a friend of Bohuslav's. I told her I had been talking to Bohuslav the day before and mentioned that I planned to go to Pisek the next day. He was delighted and asked me to extend an invitation to her and her son to a picnic that he was having the following Sunday. She thanked me for the message, but she said it would be impossible for her to accept it because she had to work as a cleaning woman every morning. In the afternoons and on Sundays, she had to do her own housework. I could see she was disappointed at not being able to go. She asked me to sit down and visit with her awhile. She seemed glad to have someone to talk with. She told me that she was originally from my home town and she knew a little of my parent's families and our neighbors. We chatted awhile about them, and then I turned the conversation to her family.

She told me that she had lived in Pisek since her marriage and seldom got back to visit her old friends and relatives. Her husband had died many years ago, leaving her with two sons to raise. She fondly reminisced about her older son, Jan, who lived in Australia at that time.

"Jan was a restless boy who loved adventure. He had no real reason, but in 1949, he escaped for the sheer thrill of the adventure. I seldom hear from him anymore," she sighed heavily, "but still he was a good boy—much better than the younger one. When Jan was home, he gave me money every month and he worked hard. But this one—this young one— he is different. He doesn't like to work and he never gives me one korun even when I ask for it. And yet I feed him; I wash for him and clean up after him; but still he won't obey me. *Never* does he set foot in church; he would rather get drunk somewhere. I get so provoked at him. What am I to do,

I love him. After all, he is my son and so I keep on doing everything for him."

I listened intently as she talked on freely, "What bothers me most is that he joined the Communist Party. He never mentioned it to me, of course. But someone told me that he even works with the S. T. B. Can you imagine that—my own son working for the S. T. B.? That rascal!" she exclaimed. "Lately he has money but he won't work anywhere. Where he gets it, I don't know. But it bothered me, so I asked him where he gets his money. He became very angry and told me it is none of my business. Imagine talking to me, his own mother, like that."

I felt sorry for the lady, but I was horrified when she mentioned his collaboration with the S. T. B. That explained many things. I knew then why he was always putting us off. It was evident that he was playing a double game. Franta was a parasite, bleeding all the money he could from us. When we no longer had anything to give, he would turn us over to the S. T. B. and collect a reward from them.

I realized that not only was the money that we had already given him lost, but it was evident that we must leave as soon as possible.

Mrs. Franta was chattering lightly by then about some mutual friend. I nodded pleasantly at her, pretending to listen, but all the while, I was trying to devise a new plan. While she was still talking, we heard the back door slam. She gasped and fervently said, "That's him now. Please, don't mention what I told you."

"Don't worry, I won't," I assured her. Little did she know that my safety depended on neither of us repeating our conversation.

Franta looked startled as he entered the room and saw me, but his mother did not notice.

"Oh, Franta, come here. I want you to meet Peter Esterka," she said pleasantly. "Peter is from my old home town and he knows so many of my old friends. Peter told me that our old friend, Mr. Bohuslav, sent us his greetings and an invitation to come to a picnic he is planning next Sunday. He wants you to come, too, isn't that nice?"

Franta nodded a reply but did not comment, neither did he look directly at me. I could see he was disturbed to see me in his home. I noticed that Mrs. Franta tried so hard to please her son.

"Sit down, boys, and we can talk a little," Mrs. Franta urged.

We chatted a little longer. After a little while, I said that I would have to be leaving. As I turned to leave, I winked at Franta. He understood and said he had to go downtown. I offered him a ride on the motorcycle and he accepted.

A few blocks from his house, I stopped and said,

"I hated to have to come here, but I'm sure no one followed me."

"I wish you hadn't come to my house. My mother gets so nosey," Franta snapped.

"It's all right. That story about Bohuslav's picnic was real enough for her. She doesn't suspect a thing."

"I hope not. But don't come here again."

"Franta, I had to see you, I'm getting more nervous all the time." What I told him was true. "They've found a replacement for me at the *internat*. They haven't said anything to me about being fired yet, but a Party member has been snooping around my job. They're having me show him everything. As soon as he learns how to instruct the apprentices, he will be ready to replace me. Can't you understand that I *must* go now? I've got a little more money to give you today. Pepek will give you the rest of the 8,000 korun the next time he sees you."

Franta took my money without a word or without looking at me. I knew that it was futile to give him any more money, but I hoped more money would convince him that I didn't suspect his double game. At that point, I was sure of only one thing; if Franta became suspicious, we were lost.

195

"When can we go, Franta?"

"This next Sunday for sure."

"Can I count on it?"

"You have my word."

I left Franta and immediately phoned Pepek to meet me in Zamky as soon as he could get there.

Together we came to a decision:

According to Franta's plan, we were not supposed to go any sooner than Sunday night. That meant we still had two more nights that we could risk trying to go on our own. It was Thursday, but we did not have time to go that night. That meant we had either Friday or Saturday night. Personally, I thought it would be much better to go Friday night because we never knew what would happen in one day.

"We have nothing to lose if we go tomorrow, and each day we delay means more risks," Pepek agreed, "so let's try tomorrow."

"Do you have everything ready that I told you to prepare?" Pepek nodded.

"Then we will meet tomorrow afternoon about three at the railroad station here. O. K.?"

"One more problem," Pepek reflected slowly. "I just got a letter today from one of the boys I knew in college. He will be passing through, so he said he will stop here tonight to see me. But I think he will leave tomorrow morning because he mentioned something about an examination he has to take tomorrow night."

"Look, Pepek, it is your friend and your problem. Be sure he does leave in the morning. It is up to you to let him 'decide' to leave early."

Leaving Pepek, I went to the *internat* to take a good rest because I knew the next day would be a hard one for us.

As I entered the *internat,* Comrade Holub and one of the men from the factory bustled past me. They were talking about a machine breaking down in the factory and didn't acknowledge my greeting.

196

Going past Comrade Holub's office, I noticed the door was slightly ajar, so I waited until I was sure they were gone, and I went inside. He would not be back very soon if there was trouble in the factory. I was surprised to find the safe open. Usually Comrade Holub was most scrupulous about the safe. But most surprising of all, the key was left in the lock of a compartment in the safe. I had mentally dubbed the compartment "mysterious" because every time Comrade Holub needed something from the compartment when I was in the room, he would ask me to leave and then he locked the door behind me. Naturally I was curious as to what was kept in it. Opening the compartment I found two pistols, a sub-machine gun, gas masks, the *cadre cards* of the staff and apprentices of the *internat,* and most important of all, Comrade Holub's signature stamp, and the seals of the *internat,* the union of the factory, and the Communist Party.

Such a discovery on that particular night was fantastic!

I stole some stationery with the *internat's* letterhead and typed: "Peter Esterka has my permission to be excused from the *internat* until Wednesday. He is representing our county in the track meet in Budejovice." I stamped Comrade Holub's signature at the bottom and put the *internat's* seal and the seal of the union next to the signature. Next I stamped some blank sheets with the seals.

I was sorely tempted to take the two pistols, but decided against it. If we were caught with weapons in our possession, we could be treated as hardened criminals.

I replaced the seals and relocked the safe, leaving everything exactly as I found it. I went to my room with what might very well be my only passport.

The next morning instead of going home as I usually did when I worked the evening shift, I went to Mass. Pepek was also there. Kneeling beside him was a young man who went to confession and Holy Communion as Pepek and I did. I knew he must be the friend Pepek was talking about the night before.

197

After Mass, we met in the front of the church. Pepek introduced me to his friend, Jara. Then he asked to speak to me alone. We walked aside and Pepek told me Jara had found out about our plan and he wanted to go along. Pepek explained that when Jara had come, Pepek invited him to spend the night with him.

"While I took my bath, Jara asked where my fingernail clippers were. I completely forgot about the other things I had hidden and without thinking, I said 'In my sport satchel.' Jara found the clippers all right, but he also found the insulated wire cutters, the map, the pepper—everything. Of course, he asked several questions, I stammered around and couldn't answer. Finally he said he knows what the things are for. He asked if he could go along with me. I explained that it didn't completely depend on me. He knows by now that you are the one who has to make the final decision."

"Does he have any reason for going with us?"

"He said he has many relatives in the United States. Another reason he gave me is that he wants to be a medical doctor, but because his relatives are living in America, he was sent to the mechanical college."

"Does he realize the dangers of this business?"

"I think he does."

"What do you think? Do we take him along or not?"

"I think it would be better to take him with us than to leave him. He knows too much already, and for us it is the same," Pepek noted. "If he wants to take the risks, let him come along."

We joined Jara and reluctantly I said, "Pepek told me that you know about our plan. He said that you would like to come along. O. K. Come. But remember, the whole responsibility is yours. Understand that we are going by ourselves with no other help. There is a tremendous risk. If we are caught, it could mean long prison terms. And there is a bigger risk that we could be shot on sight near the border.

Actually, the possibility that we will make it is very, very small. I think you should realize it. Before you make up your mind, think all this over very carefully. You must decide for yourself. You have several hours to think about it. If you decide to go, be with Pepek at the railroad station in Zamky."

Then I went home.

19. "GOOD-BY"

My last hours at home with my family were filled with mixed emotions. I was torn between my desire to escape and my reluctance to leave them. To stay was impossible—to leave was infinitely as difficult.

We had always been a close knit family, but I was causing an emptiness for them that could never be filled.

We had always discussed all my major plans very thoroughly, except my escape. That I could not tell them. Not because I did not want to. God knows how I wanted to ask their permission and their blessing on my plans. But if I were caught, certainly the S.T.B. would try to involve whomever they could. If my parents knew nothing of my stealthy activities, they could not be blamed for the actions of their impetuous son.

After dinner I went into my room to pack. Whenever I had left for an extended time before, Mother had always packed for me, but that time I didn't want her to see what I was doing. From the pocket of my winter overcoat where I had hidden them months before I took the pair of electrician's rubber gloves and the insulated wire cutters. Carefully I packed them between my other clothes at the bottom of the satchel. On top of them, I packed a complete change of clothes and my track suit and shoes. On one side, I carefully placed the "excuse" I had typed in the *internat* the night before and my certificate verifying that I had been in the finals in the national races.

As I zipped the satchel closed and started for the door, I dolefully looked around the room that had been home to me my entire life. On the shelf in the corner was my soccer ball and the other memorabilia of my youth. In the bookcase was my cherished collection of books that I fondly referred to as my "library" even though it contained only a few books. Everything in my room was as I had always kept it, but I would never return again to see it. One last gaze, a sigh, and I closed the door quickly and walked into the kitchen.

I tried to hide my satchel from my mother's view. Mother was well aware that when I ordinarily went to stay for a few days in the *internat,* I usually took along only something to eat because I kept the necessary clothes there.

Mother instinctively looked at me and then at the bulging satchel in my hand. She eyed me suspiciously for a moment. I knew she would ask questions and I feverishly tried to think of logical answers. When Mother suspected something was amiss, she was more ingenious than the S. T. B. at getting answers from me. It always baffled me how she seemed to know even what I was thinking.

"For heaven's sake, Peta, what do you have in the satchel today?"

I had never been able to lie and get by with it, but I answered, "I'm going to a track meet tomorrow so I'm taking some things with me." I knew it was a poor lie, but I couldn't think of a better one at the moment.

How glad I would have been if I could have told her what was going on! How much better I would have felt if I could have only kissed her at that moment, or at least told her that I would not be back and ask her to pray for my success! But it was impossible. Not only she, but no one else, could know about our plan. My emotions were locked within and words failed me. I still cannot find words to explain what I felt at that moment when I was leaving home forever.

As I said, even if I could fool everyone else, I could not fool Mother. It was impossible for her to know exactly what was going on, but I feel certain that she somehow knew, or at least had a premonition of what I was doing.

Mother picked up a sack of kolaches that she had packed

for me (she knew how to bake kolaches better than anyone on earth), and handed them to me without a word.

I opened my satchel and removed my track shoes to make room for the kolaches. She didn't ask why I had packed my track shoes inside instead of slinging them over the top of the satchel as I usually did. She didn't ask anything more. She just looked at me, her eyes longing for an explanation. It was a long searching look. I felt like she was trying to read my heart. For only an instant, her look was suspicious, then, like a dark cloud passing over her sweet face, I could see she began to worry.

"Shall I try to explain to you, Mother? Couldn't I at least tell you not to worry?" I loved her too much to say the words aloud. No, it wouldn't be wise. She and my whole family could get into trouble if they knew. "It was better to leave like this," I decided.

Carrying the satchel in one hand and holding Mother in my other arm, we reached the door and I summoned enough will-power to hoarsely say, "Good-by, Mother."

"Good-by, Peta."

She drew me closely to herself. She held me tightly for a long moment. I could feel a tear trickle from her cheek onto my own. Without a word, she reached into the holy water font that we kept near the door and made the sign of the cross on my forehead. Only twice before had she blessed me in that way—when I left to go to the seminary as a boy and when I left to enter the *internat* the first time. I was overwhelmed with emotion.

Mother kissed me lovingly and whispered, "Be a good boy." Her voice trembled and I noticed the tears in her eyes. But it was only for a moment. She blinked them away and turned to Anynka who was standing beside us in wonderment at what she was witnessing. No other farewell was ever so poignant for us before. "Tell Peta good-by, Anynka."

Anynka hugged me tenderly and said, "Good-by, Peta."

I was so choked up that I couldn't speak.

We walked outside into the bright sunshine. July is an especially beautiful time of year in Czechoslovakia and the beauty of that day will live forever in my heart even though my heart was heavier than it ever had been before. I remember seeing things that I had always taken for granted, and they are still keenly imprinted in my memory.

"Frantik, come here," Mother called to my little brother, who was playing in the yard with the neighbor's children. Frantik came running toward us as another boy playfully chased him. He didn't intend to stop, but Anynka stepped in his way, grabbed him, and pushed him toward me.

"Tell Peta good-by," she told him solemnly.

"Good-by," Frantik yelled, trying to get loose so that he could join his friends again. But Anynka held him.

"Shake hands with Peta," she insisted, sensing that something was not as it should be.

Frantik was seven and loved to play grown-up and shake hands. We had often made a game of it. So he stuck out his hand in a grown-up way and smiled heartily.

"Give him some sugar, Frantik," Mother suggested.

I grabbed Frantik into my arms and pulled him to my height. He gave me a big "smack" and jumped down to run and play with his friends.

I turned back to my mother and sister and said a last, "Good-by."

"Good-by," I heard them both say as I quickly turned away. I couldn't look at Mother's face any longer.

I felt sure Mother didn't know exactly what was happening, but still her motherly instinct. . . .

I got to the bus station just a few minutes before the bus was ready to leave. I noticed my father was sitting between two of his friends in the rear of the bus. He was working the evening shift that day, but it was always his custom to be at the bus station at least fifteen minutes before the bus

203

was due to leave. That's why he was gone when I left home. He had a favorite saying: "It is better to wait half an hour than to be one minute late."

I nodded and gave a little greeting with my hand. He smiled back.

I took a seat next to a window and watched the familiar scenes pass before me for the last time. The streets I had walked on all my life, the homes of our friends, and best of all, my own home. Standing outside my home were my mother and sister waving to me as the bus went by. I shall never forget it.

Then we passed the church, the focal point of my life, where I was baptized, confirmed, attended Mass, received Communion, and penance; and possibly from which I would have been buried had I chosen to spend my life in my own country. The view of the church was framed by the green trees and presented an indelible sight.

In a few minutes we were beyond the town on the highway that was lined with cherry trees. Reaching the top of a hill, I looked back and saw my native village nestled in its green valley and the steeple of the church tower rising in its last farewell.

When we reached the factory gate in Zamky, my father got off the bus to go to work. As he walked passed me, he paused only an instant and sighed, "Good-by, Peta, my son."

"Good-by . . ."

20. ESCAPE

At 3:30 p.m. I went to the railroad station in Zamky. Both Pepek and Jara were waiting there. I immediately saw how nervous they were.

"What's wrong?" I asked.

"Look at the policeman there," whispered Pepek. "I think he is watching us."

"Don't be a fool. He can't read your thoughts."

"But don't forget about Franta," he said nervously.

He was right, there was the question of Franta. But I was pretty sure that he was enjoying the money that we had already given him, and was waiting to get the rest of the 8,000 korun from us Sunday—and how much would he get from the S. T. B.? Who knows?

"This is no time to worry about Franta. Do you have everything with you?"

"Yes, I do. In case we have to separate, here is your ticket."

The tickets were for Budejovice, a large city far enough from the Austrian border so as not to call special attention to our destination. Of course, we did not plan to go all the way to Budejovice. We wanted to ride only as far as Mikulov because the station in Mikulov was situated only a few hundred yards from the border. We felt that we had the best chance to escape at that point. The only problem involved was that Mikulov is in the border territory—a guarded strip of land that runs the entire length of the border.

Besides the dangers such as guards, dogs, signal apparatus, mines, machine-gun towers, and electric wires, another real danger was the people. Only those who were members of the border patrol, the Communist Party, or the S. T. B., or their collaborators were allowed to live *there*. Anyone else who wished to pass through the border territory was closely checked before he could receive special permission to enter. We knew it was too dangerous for us even to apply for permission, for we had no excuse for wanting to go there. Nonetheless, we knew from the beginning that it was imperative that we have some justifiable excuse for being in the territory should we be caught. Our only excuse would be that we were on our way to a track meet in Budejovice. We didn't know whether Budejovice was having a track meet, and we hoped the guards didn't either. I took along the forged papers which I had from the *internat* the night before, and also my certificate verifying that I had been in the finals in the national races. Pepek had his certificate for being a county winner in the 1,000 meter run. Unfortunately Jara had no credentials whatsoever. Yet he had one real asset—a good athletic physique. He was very muscular and taller than either Pepek or I. He looked like a natural discus thrower, so he planned to claim to be one, on his way to the meet with us.

So without proper papers, we left Zamky about 3.20 p.m. A few minutes before 6:00, we were in Znojmo where we were to change trains. Znojmo has a rather large railroad station with which I was quite familiar because I went there several times when I thought it would be possible to escape on the train.

We had a one-hour lay-over in Znojmo. Since the station was partially under the border guard control, we needed to be extremely vigilant. So as not to attract attention, I separated from Pepek and Jara. I noticed several soldiers patrolling with their watch dogs and automatic guns. Away from the terminal on a separate track was a train ready to leave for Austria. While the people inside looked from their windows, the guards with dogs guarded it on both sides.

Trying to look as calm and natural as possible, I went into the station's restaurant and ordered a soft drink and ice cream. Then I walked a little in the park in front of the station and bought a newspaper. I returned to the station, and sitting on a bench in the hall, I tried to read my paper. My nerves did not permit me to concentrate much, for I was suspicious of every man I saw. Any one of them could have been an S. T. B. agent.

"Hello, Peter, how are you?" I heard a feminine voice say. Turning around, I saw a group of girls standing behind me. The one who spoke was Draha, my classmate from high school. I did not know the others.

"Hi, how are you?" I asked, little taken aback.

Draha introduced me to her friends, and asked what I was doing there.

"Waiting for the train to Budejovice," I replied.

"That's wonderful. I'm going in the same direction. We can ride together about thirty-five minutes."

I was greatly relieved when Draha assured me that she was going only a short way. I hate to think what might have happened had Draha lived in Mikulov or farther.

By this time Pepek and Jara had joined us. Talking to the girls made the time pass quickly and for a little while, as we talked, I forgot about the dangers we were facing. All too soon the thoughts of mounting dangers returned as I saw the border guard scrupulously watching our train.

The loud-speaker announced that the train for Budejovice was ready on the third track. Some of the passengers were forced to show their tickets and permissions as they boarded the train, but we were lucky. It was probably because we were going in a whole crowd. Some of the girls were going in the opposite direction, but five of them went with us on the train to Budejovice. I noticed one of the girls flirted a little with one of the officers as she got on board.

We occupied one small compartment on the train. Every thing looked normal as we joked and laughed. As the guards passed by, one of the girls opened the door and teasingly said something to them. The guards did not suspect the whole crowd, so we were safe as long as our group was together. Thank God for the good fortune we had in meeting the girls.

Three girls got off the train before Draha did. Later Draha left us, too, wishing us success in our track meet. Now only one of the girls was still with us, but she too would leave before we reached Mikulov.

Once, before we reached Mikulov, we passed the Iron Curtain so closely that we could see three separate rows of obstacles and two machine-gun towers. "So *that* is the Iron Curtain," I thought. "It is the most terrifying thing I have ever seen." I shuddered at its very sight.

Soon the sun began to set slowly in a magnificent sunset. It was the last time I saw the sun shine on my native country, and it made me sorely melancholy.

A little later two old women and a young girl came into our compartment. They started to talk about a celebration they had been to and then mentioned some lady's name and told how her husband, who escaped several years ago, had gone to the United States and was doing very well. They spoke somberly of other people who escaped and who were living in Australia, Canada, or the United States.

"But now it is impossible to get through," remarked one old lady.

"Yes, I know. Just last week we heard shooting and saw the signal rockets," said the other one.

"No, today it is better not to try anything like that. There are too many obstacles. There are mine fields, too, but nobody knows where they are."

The ladies continued their grim conversation which was anything but encouraging to us. I found myself wondering if they suspected us, or if their conversation was natural. At that point I was suspicious of everyone.

As the ladies continued to talk about the dangers of the border territory (which we had already entered), I could see through the windows of the door that the guards had come into the coach in front of ours to inspect permissions.

They were coming closer and closer. Soon they would be in our coach and we would be in real peril unless something happened.

Pepek and Jara were sitting on the bench opposite the older ladies and me. They could not see the guards but I noticed that they had changed—their faces were pale and they seemed petrified. I, too, did not feel very well. I listened only slightly to what the ladies were saying, but my attention was fixed on the guards as they steadily approached us. I felt my stomach somewhere in my throat. I had a terrible feeling I can't explain even today. I don't know whether it was fear or not—I had been afraid before, but I had never felt that way, nor have since. My two friends told me later they felt the same way. Every time I have a dream about my escape, I do not dream about the actual crossing of the border, but about the train and the time I spent there watching the approaching guards. They were coming still closer and closer.

The guards had just come into our coach and had gone into the first compartment, when I saw several lights in front of us. It was Mikulov. I stood up and I nodded slightly to my friends.

"Good-by, ladies," my voice sounded strange even to me.

My two companions followed me to the far end of our coach where it was little darker.

"Look, there are the lights of Mikulov," Pepek exclaimed.

As we approached Mikulov, the train began to slow down. It had now almost reached the outskirts of the town.

"The guards are already in the first compartment of our coach," I opened the door. The wind blew in our faces. "Let's go." I jumped out of the train. The other two followed.

No one was hurt and luckily we jumped when the train had almost reached the outskirts of the town. By jumping when we did, we not only eluded the guards on the train, we also evaded those at the station.

We knew that the border was to the south, but we were

afraid to approach it directly because the fields between the station and the border were probably watched most closely after a train passed through. Anyone who saw three strange boys loitering in the border territory would easily suspect what we were up to. We felt that our best chance was to mingle with other passengers and go with them toward the center of the town. We were able to catch up with them and intersperse among them as they left the station. I am not sure why it took them so long before they left the station—perhaps they had to pass an inspection. But we noticed a strange sort of silence among the other passengers. The whole town was ominously silent. We saw very few people. Only the music and voices from the radios and the sounds of the cows and dogs gave any evidence that anyone lived in the town.

Because Pepek knew Mikulov pretty well, he was our guide. He thought that our best plan would be to go toward the center of the town in the direction of the old castle. From there we could make a wide circle and leave Mikulov on the north-east side, and only after we left the town would we head south toward the border.

We had almost walked through Mikulov when Pepek led us down a narrow street he thought would lead us out of the town. The street led instead to an oblong courtyard which was surrounded by barracks. On the courtyard were two volleyball courts and soldiers' obstacle training equipment. Realizing it was the quarters of the border guards, we turned and quietly fled back to the main street. As we approached the intersection, we were appalled by the lights of a car coming toward us. We flattened ourselves in the shadows of the wall of the building until the patrol car disappeared in the darkness. Frantically, we hurried down the street in the direction from which the car had come. The houses on the street formed a solid wall on both sides of the street for several hundred yards. There was no place for us to hide in case the patrol car returned. That particular street was the highway that went through the town. Panic striken, we took the first exit from the street even though it turned left when we wanted to turn right toward the south.

We scampered down the narrow alley that soon became only a lane which led to a vineyard. There we checked to make sure all of our escape paraphernalia was ready. To lighten our load, we discarded everything that could not be put into one satchel. Before starting out again, we prayed an Our Father, a Hail Mary, and I said aloud the prayer my mother had taught me when we were begging for help during the war. Whenever I was in dread peril, I prayed most fervently:

"Remember, O most gracious Virgin Mary, that never was it known that anyone who fled to your protection, implored your help, and sought your intercession, was left unaided! Inspired with this confidence, I fly unto you, O Virgin of virgins, my Mother! To you I come. Before you I stand, sinful and sorrowful. O Mother of the Word Incarnate, despise not my petitions, but in your mercy hear and answer me! Amen."

We were sure now in which direction from the vineyard the border lay, but we did not know how far it was.

"Peter, it's your turn to be the leader now. I'm too scared to think straight," Pepek declared.

"All right," I agreed. "But from here on there's no excuse that we can give the guards for being out here. They are certainly not stupid, so whatever we do, let's keep low."

The moon was just starting to rise very brightly. Its light made it easier for us to see—and be seen.

We left the cover of the vineyard and went into a sort of pasture where many small bushes grew. We made our way in a stooping kind of run from bush to bush taking cover in their shadows. After only a little while, we came to the highway that we had left in our haste.

211

On the other side of the highway was a wheat field in which the wheat was not fully grown. The wheat was barely tall enough to hide us when we crept on our knees and forearms. Jara suggested that we form a single line, and insisted on being in the middle because he said he had forgotten his glasses and could not see very well. Later he told us the real reason was that he didn't want to be last in line. "I could feel the dog's teeth on my throat" was his reasoning. We couldn't let him go first because he moved with only a little less agility and finesse than a tank. So Pepek took the lead while I strapped the satchel to my chest and brought up the rear.

Whenever we stopped to rest a little, I sprinkled pepper behind us to ward off the dogs who might pick up our scent.

At approximately midnight, and after what seemed an interminably long three hours of crawling, Jara said, "I can't go any farther. Let's go back. Please. I'm too tired to make it."

"Don't be a fool. We can't go back now," I whispered. "We threw out our things and they'll find them sooner or later."

"I don't care. I just can't go any more."

"You should have thought of that before you started out. Let's go."

"Please, can't we rest some more?"

"O. K. O.K., let's rest a little longer. But forget about going back anymore."

Pepek didn't say one word. We rested longer than usual, we prayed to the Blessed Mother and Saint Jude, the patron of hopeless cases. How much better one can pray when one is really in need! The words we had said so many times before meant so much, much more to me that night. When I was saying, "Remember, O most gracious Virgin Mary, that never was it known that anyone who fled was left unaided . . ." I was really begging with all my heart. I meant every word I said.

But we all were so tired—so very tired. We were actually numb. We wanted to rest, to sleep, maybe even quit. At this point we didn't care what happened, and yet we instinctively knew—like a hunted animal—that we had to go on. It was impossible to quit.

Lying there on the ground of the wheat field, Jara started again, "Maybe we still have time to go back. I'm terribly tired. I don't care what will happen to me."

"Maybe he's right, Peta. We don't know how much farther it is and we are all so tired. What do you think about going back to the vineyard and getting our things and going home before we are missed? Maybe we can try again later," Pepek moaned.

"Are you crazy? There will never be a 'later' for us, and you know it. We are in the border territory and it is as hard to get out of here as it is to get in. Even if we could get home, there is still Franta and his taste for money."

"Pepek, what do you say?" Jara asked.

"He's right, Jara. It is impossible to go back, so shut up."

Raising myself a little, I tried to see the end of the field. There was nothing but wheat. Just one big sea of wheat. We all began to feel a little sick. It was already about one o'clock, and we couldn't see the border or even the railroad embankment that we knew we would have to cross before we got to the border itself. According to our calculations, we should have already been crossing the border by that time,

We moved a few yards again and then rested, moved and rested, moved and rested. After each rest, I spinkled some more pepper. But by that time we were moving forward much slower than we had been in the beginning. The moves were much shorter and the rests much longer. I began to use the pepper more sparingly. I had to save some for later.

At about a quarter to two, we finally reached the end of the wheat field. We rested again—a little longer than usual.

A stretch of open land was beyond, but we had no camouflage anymore, so we had to crawl on our stomachs, making our progress even slower. The satchel seemed to get heavier by the yard.

Next, we entered a sugar beet field and the going became easier again. The ground had been plowed and the shadows of the furrows gave a little protection. Again we could partially crawl. We broke our follow-the-leader style and crawled beside each other. It seemed that we had caught a second breath by then and our progress quickened considerably.

"I would like to have a glass of water," complained Jara as he took a sugar beet leaf and started to chew it to quench his thirst.

Why did he have to say aloud what we were all thinking! Before my mind's eye was a glass of cool, sparkling water.

"Jara, will you quit complaining?" I snapped.

"I just said that I wish I had some water."

"Quit that arguing, you two," Pepek chided, "There's the railroad embankment just ahead. Be very careful; the guards may be near."

So we moved forward quietly.

The question of whether the Iron Curtain was only a few yards beyond the embankment kept plaguing me. I prayed that it was. It *had* to be.

In that part of the world, daybreak comes very early in July, so that by 3:00 a.m., the very first rays of dawn begin to break. Soon the sun would be up and the guards could look down and see us groveling on the ground, and all would be lost.

Slowly, very slowly, I crept to the top of the railroad embankment, and much more slowly, I raised my head to see what was beyond, thinking all the while that the top of my head could be blown off as it cleared the summit. But I was not prepared for what I did see. My heart stopped beating at the sight of a machine-gun tower that loomed in front of us. It was so close that it seemed we were almost under it. I could see the silhouettes of the soldiers as they moved around. I could also see that a large area around the

214

tower was closely mowed. In the ever increasing daylight, I could see that just beyond the tower were three rows of wire obstacle fences. About eighty yards to the left was a small wheat field.

Quietly I moved back down to Pepek and Jara and motioned them to follow me along the embankment. Jara, with super strength that comes with panic, was soon ahead of us both. It took very little time to crawl that particular eighty or so yards.

In the shadows, we checked the gloves and wire cutters for the last time. Since we had only two cutters, Pepek took one and I kept the other and the rubber gloves. I used the last of the pepper.

We had to be very careful crossing the embankment and railroad tracks because one clumsy move would alert the guard who could see our silhouettes against the sky.

We quickly crawled into the small wheat field on the other side of the tracks. As we reached the middle of the field (about forty or fifty yards from the border), we heard a shot. We pasted ourselves to the ground—face down. The shot turned out to be a signal rocket. I couldn't resist looking up to see the weird light that the rocket cast. The rocket reached its zenith and burned out before it reached the ground.

"Now what?" I thought. "Lie down and don't move."

I could hear my heart beating and my breathing and that of my friends seemed to resound in the stillness.

Soon in the distance, we heard voices coming closer.

"They're coming for us," I froze at the thought.

The voices and steps came very close to the place where we lay. What thoughts raced through my mind during that eternity are beyond explanation.

The footsteps came close—so very close. They were upon us. And then passed us by.

For several moments, no one moved a muscle.

Finally Pepek said, "Let's get out of here. They don't

215

know we are here. We have only a few minutes left before the sun comes up over the mountains."

We could clearly see that beyond the wheat field was a space of about fifteen yards between us and the Iron Curtain. The space was carefully raked and particularly well cared for.

"Is it . . . kept raked so that the guards can see if someone crosses it, or is it rigged with mines?" Jara asked.

We did not know. We had no time or way to tell, and no alternative but to plunge through it.

We were within a few yards of the formidable fences themselves. There were three separate fences. The first one held four rows of electric wires which were extended ten to twelves inches on the inner side of the fence by insulators. On the Austrian side of the same fence were plaited barbed wires that were criss-crossed back and forth many times. The two fences were not electrified, but the criss-cross, twisted barbed wires were much closer together—almost like a web.

And beyond those barbed wires—*freedom*.

Before we ventured into the raked strip, we checked our assignments for the last time. It was then that I discovered that the rubber gloves were gone. I had probably left them lying in the field after our scare by the guards.

"Pepek, you cut the lowest electric wire and I will take care of the second one. Then we will try to make room in the next wires. Jara, take this satchel and follow us."

A last few minutes of rest, a last Hail Mary, and we were ready to penetrate the impenetrable Iron Curtain.

"Peter, say the prayer to the Blessed Mother again," Jara insisted just before we started to move again. It was odd. Jara was not ordinarily a religious boy. Probably he went to Mass every Sunday, but he was not especially conscientious about his other duties as a Catholic. And still, in the time of great danger, he somehow felt God's presence and the need of God's help much more than either Pepek or I.

Pepek lay on his back listening to the prayer and looking

upward. I said my mother's prayer again—God Himself knows that I meant every word of it.

".. despise not my petitions, but in your mercy hear and answer me! Amen."

Just as I finished, Pepek whispered hurriedly, "Look, there is something right in front of us."

"Where?"

"*Be careful, Jara!*"

"Look, right here," Pepek pointed. "But you have to lie flat on the ground to see it against the sky."

I lay down next to Pepek, and there it was—just a few inches from our heads—a shiny wire, placed about two feet from the ground.

"What's it there for?" Jara asked. "Is the wire connected to mines or only to a signal apparatus?"

"What difference does it make? If we touch it, we're dead."

Even if it was only a signal, it was as bad as if it were a mine. To touch it would immediately bring down the fire from the machine gun tower. And we were so close to the tower, it was almost impossible for the guards to miss us.

"Just be very careful. We have to jump over it. Can you see the wire, Jara?"

"Yes, I do."

Thank God no one touched it as we stepped over it.

By then, the sun was coming up very fast. We had only a few minutes left to cross the border. The distance was so small, but we didn't know how many more "surprises" we could expect. My nerves were extremely tense, and yet I was aware of even the slightest stir or sound around us. Fortunately, everything was very still, and best of all, we were moving smoothly and silently.

Pepek and I crawled to the first fence and put our cutters to the electric wires. A shower of sparks erupted. The wires were charged with electricity all right. I ardently wished we still had the rubber gloves. We put the insulated cutters to the wire, bore down, and the wires fell to the ground with a

217

terrific shower of sparks and a low searing sound. We waited for some movement from the tower. All was quiet.

Then we cut the maze of twisted barbed wires and crawled through the first fence.

We cut the wires in the second fence. There were many more wires in it but none that were charged with electricity, so we could work fast. Our clothes were tearing and our skin was being pricked by the sharp points, but we didn't notice or care. Our one thought was to hurry and get through the third fence.

Just a moment later Pepek and I stood beyond the three fences as Jara was still struggling through the last one. We helped him through and then we ran as fast as we could. Jara, who was usually slower than either of us, passed us both. As we ran, I saw a stone that was the actual dividing line between Czechoslovakia and Austria.

In that moment I was the happiest man in the world. Freedom was ours.

From the tower there was nothing—no searchlights, no rockets, no shots, no dogs barking—only silence.

With torn clothes and pricked skin; with laughing hearts and misty eyes; and our native soil still embedded upon us, we stood on a small knoll in Austria looking back beyond barbed wires into Czechoslovakia—to our native country, where we spent our childhood and our teenage years; to our homeland, where we left our parents, sisters, relatives, friends . . .

The country we just left—our homeland—was only some two hundred yards from us, but it was in another world, sealed by the Iron Curtain.

As the sun came up from behind the mountains, a new day dawned—and for us—a new, free life.

EPILOGUE

Along with our newly found freedom, a choice of all the wonderful opportunities of the whole world was suddenly within our grasp.

Pepek and Jara chose to emigrate to the United States, the sanctuary of which they had dreamed.

From a refugee camp where I spent three months contemplating how I wanted to spend my life, I went to Rome to study for the priesthood. Since I had so recently left a life distorted by hate and godlessness, it seemed natural that the rest of my life should be devoted to God's love and service.

After six years of study, I was ordained a priest on March 9, 1963—by coincidence, the millennium of the Christianization of my homeland—in the Basilica of St. John Lateran. Among those who were with me the next day to share the joys of my first Mass were many new friends and Pepek (who, by that time, had also decided to become a priest and was studying in Rome). But those whom I wanted to be with me the most were missing—my beloved parents, Anynka, Frantik, and all my relatives and friends who were still confined within my country.

After coming to the United States and having relished freedom to the fullest, I see how glorious and precious freedom really is. I pray that some day the wires that entangle the border will be disentwined, and the hearts and minds of all mankind will at last be free.